P9-DFU-048

CHICKEN SOUP FOR THE CHIROPRACTIC SOUL

Stories of Inspiration Healing, Laughter and a Lifetime of Wellness

Jack Canfield
Mark Victor Hansen
Dr. Fabrizio Mancini

Health Communications, Inc.
Deerfield Beach, Florida

www.hcibooks.com
www.chickensoup.com

We would like to acknowledge the following publishers and individuals for permission to reprint the following material. (Note: The stories that were penned anonymously, that are public domain, or that were written by Jack Canfield, Mark Victor or Dr. Fabrizio Mancini are not included in this listing.)

Joy and Redemption. Reprinted by permission of Buddy Levy and Dan O'Brien. ©2002 Buddy Levy.

The Baseball Story. Reprinted by permission of Dr. Jeffrey D. Conner and Dawn Planty. ©2002 Dawn Planty.

To Finish What He Started. Reprinted by permission of Caroline Reno. ©2002 Caroline Reno.

A Special Gift. Reprinted by permission of Dr. Joel Miller. ©2001 Dr. Joel Miller.

(Continued on page 239)

In the spirit of creating a healthier lifestyle through chiropractic care, a portion of the proceeds will go towards a fund for the advancement of chiropractic education, research and public relations. If you feel inspired to join us in this cause of bringing chiropractic to the ones you love with your contributions or donations please contact us at *www.chickensoup.parkerseminars.com* or (888) 772-5867. Your contributions truly will make a difference.

All rights reserved. Printed in the United States of America. No part of this publication may be reproduced, stored in a retrieval system or transmitted in any form or by any means, electronic, mechanical, photocopying, recording or otherwise, without the written permission of the publisher.

These stories hopefully provide general education, inspiration and nourishment for your soul. However, every individual and every individual's health is different. You and your health are unique, and you deserve and need the careful though and individual attention of your own doctor to determine the condition of your health and to decide how you should respond to or treat any disease or condition that you may have. No matter how entertaining and heart warming this book may be, it cannot replace a doctor-patient relaionship or provide a diagnosis, prescription or recommendation for you or your condition.

Cataloging-in-Publication Data is on file with the Library of Congress.

© 2003 Jack Canfield and Mark Victor Hansen
ISBN 0-7573-0130-4

All rights reserved. Printed in the United States of America. No part of this publication may be reproduced, stored in a retrieval system or transmitted in any form or by any means, electronic, mechanical, photocopying, recording or otherwise, without the written permission of the publisher.

HCI, its Logos and Marks are trademarks of Health Communications, Inc.

Publisher: Health Communications, Inc.
      3201 S.W. 15th Street
      Deerfield Beach, FL 33442-8190

Cover design by Dan Saucedo
Inside formatting by Dawn Von Strolley Grove

We dedicate this book to the over 25 million chiropractic patients, chiropractic practitioners, chiropractic students, chiropractic assistants and staff members.
Also, to the millions of people who will embrace the chiropractic profession after reading this book so they too can benefit from this powerful healing art and science.

The Chiropractic Oath

To hold in esteem and respect those who taught me this chiropractic healing art; to follow the methods of treatment which according to my ability and judgment I consider necessary for the benefit of my patients; to abstain from whatever is deleterious and unethical; to stand ready at all times to serve my fellow man without discrimination of race, creed or color.

With purity I will pass my life and practice my art, I will at all times consider the patients under my care as of supreme importance; I will not spare myself in rendering them the help which I have been taught to give by my alma mater; I will keep inviolate all things revealed to me as a physician.

While I continue to keep this oath inviolate, may it be granted to me to enjoy life and the practice of the chiropractic healing art, respected by all men at all times.

Contents

3. SAY GOODBYE TO PAIN

4. PEDIATRICS AND CHIROPRACTIC

5. CHIROPRACTIC AND KIDS

6. ADDED YEARS

7. BEYOND THE CALL OF DUTY

8. DEFINING MOMENTS

Acknowledgments

The path to *Chicken Soup for the Chiropractic Soul* has been made all the more beautiful by the many "companions" who have been there with us along the way. Our heartfelt gratitude to:

Our families, who have been *chicken soup* for our souls!

Inga, Travis, Riley, Christopher, Oran and Kyle for all their love and support.

Patty, Elizabeth and Melanie Hansen, for once again sharing and lovingly supporting us in creating yet another book.

Alicia, Gianni and Luciano Mancini for their patience and loving encouragement. In addition, Fabrizio's parents, Giovanni and Gladys, for their constant inspiration. Thank you to his brothers Pierluigi, Aldo and Paolo and his wonderful sisters-in-law Robin and Erin for their continued love and support.

Our publisher Peter Vegso, for his vision and commitment to bringing *Chicken Soup for the Soul* to the world.

Patty Aubery, for being there on every step of the journey, with love, laughter and endless creativity.

Heather McNamara and D'ette Corona, for producing our final manuscript with magnificent ease, finesse and care. Thanks for making the final stages of production such a breeze!

Kathy Brennan-Thompson and Leslie Riskin for their superb management of the production of this book and for their determination to secure our permissions and get everything just right.

Veronica Romero, Nancy Autio, Barbara Lomonaco, Dana Drobny, Teresa Esparza, Robin Yerian, Stephanie Thatcher, Jody Emme, Trudy Marschall, Michelle Adams, Dee Dee Romanello, Shanna Vieyra, Lisa Williams, Gina Romanello, Brittany Shaw, Dena Jacobson, Tanya Jones, Mary McKay and David Coleman, who support Jack's and Mark's businesses with skill and love.

Maria Nickless, for her enthusiastic marketing and public relations support and a brilliant sense of direction.

Patty Hansen, for her thorough and competent handling of the legal and licensing aspects of the Chicken Soup for the Soul books. You are magnificent at the challenge!

The late Dr. James W. Parker for his vision of the potential of the chiropractic profession.

Sherry Slayton for being the best assistant and for organizing Fabrizio's time so that he could stay on schedule. Dr. Dana Mackison, Pam Freeman, Anne O'Neill, Doris Schrepel and the excellent staff of Parker Seminars for their effort in sharing this book with the whole chiropractic profession. Dr. Patrick Bodnar and Richard Tibbits for their role in marketing and fulfilling all the orders. Gayle Barge, Becki Gallagher, Daniel Saucedo and Kenn Leuzinger for their creativity and web support.

Thank you to all the administration, board, students, faculty and staff of Parker College of Chiropractic for maintaining excellence in all we do.

Barbara Jindra and the business office for all the bookkeeping in this project.

Bill Nardiello for his wisdom and support. The whole chiropractic profession for their commitment in sharing this book with as many people as possible.

Laurie Hartman, for being a precious guardian of the *Chicken Soup* brand.

Christine Belleris, Allison Janse, Lisa Drucker, Susan Tobias and Kathy Grant, our editors at Health Communications, Inc., for their devotion to excellence.

Terry Burke, Tom Sand, Irena Xanthos, Lori Golden, Kelly Johnson Maragni, Karen Bailiff Ornstein, Randee Feldman, Patricia McConnell, Kim Weiss, Maria Dinoia, Paola Fernandez-Rana and Teri Peluso, the marketing, sales, administration and public relations departments at Health Communications, Inc., for doing such an incredible job supporting our books.

Tom Sand, Claude Choquette and Luc Jutras, who manage year after year to get our books transferred into thirty-six languages around the world.

The Art Department at Health Communications, Inc., for their talent, creativity and unrelenting patience in producing book covers and inside designs that capture the essence of *Chicken Soup*: Larissa Hise Henoch, Lawna Patterson Oldfield, Andrea Perrine Brower, Lisa Camp, Anthony Clausi and Dawn Von Strolley Grove.

All the *Chicken Soup for the Soul* coauthors, who make it so much of a joy to be part of this Chicken Soup family: Raymond Aaron, Matthew E. Adams, Patty and Jeff Aubrey, Kirk Autio, Nancy Mitchell Autio, Marty Becker, John Boal, Cynthia Brian, Cindy Buck, Ron Camacho, Barbara Russell Chesser, Dan Clark, Tim Clauss, Barbara De Angelis, Don Dible, Mark and Chrissy Donnelly, Irene Dunlap, Rabbi Dov Peretz Elkins, Dorothy Firman, Frances Firman Salorio, Julie Firman, Bud Gardner, Patty Hansen, Jennifer Read Hawthorne, Kimberly Kirberger, Carol Kline, Tom and Laura Lagana, Tommy LaSorda, Sharon Linnea, Dr. Fabrizio Mancini, Janet Matthews, Hanoch and Meladee McCarty, Heather McNamara, Katy

McNamara, John McPherson, Paul J. Meyer, Arline Oberst, Marion Owen, Maida Rogerson, Martin Rutte, Amy Seeger, Marci Shimoff, Sidney Slagter, Barry Spilchuk, Robin Stephens, Pat Stone, Carol Sturgulewski, Jim Tunney, LeAnn Thieman, Diana von Welanetz Wentworth and Sharon Wohlmuth.

Our glorious panel of readers who helped us make the final selections and made invaluable suggestions on how to improve the book:

Lee Anderson, Bianca Benitez, Dr. Patrick Bodnar, Tony Boudreau, Dr. Walter Brake, Dr. David Cheek, Karen Clements, David Crowell, Rodney Crews, Jack and Susan Dawson, Dr. Elizabeth Doller, Maria Dominguez, Anna Folmnsbee, Carrie Gallagher, Dr. Nicole Marie Georman, Dr. Gene Giggleman, Jesse Green, Dr. Ken Hansen, Dr.Nicole Lederman, John Norfleet, Dr. James B. Parker, Kevin Priestly, Jim McChesney, January Mierzejewski, Andrea Robles, Paula Robinson, Amy Rogers, Michelle Roscoe, Dr. Ron Rupert, Marcelle Skeete, Hope Skinner, Darrell Slabaugh, Sheryl Sodorff, Dr. Al and Jeanne States, Dr. Neil Stern, Becky Sullivan, Saundra Vandervorf, David Warth and Opal West.

Dr. Frank A. Corbo, Donald K. Case and Greg Flores at Chiropractic Wellness and Fitness magazine for their help in securing and writing several of the stories.

Thank you to Daniel Saucedo for his wonderful cover artwork.

And, most of all, everyone who submitted their heartfelt stories, poems, quotes and cartoons for possible inclusion in this book. While we were not able to use everything you sent in, we know that each word came from a magical place flourishing within your soul. May the spirit of nature carry you gently towards peace!

Because of the size of this project, we may have left out the names of some people who contributed along the way.

If so, we are sorry, but please know that we really do appreciate you very much.

We are truly grateful and love you all!

Introduction

It is our deepest pleasure to offer you *Chicken Soup for the Chiropractic Soul.*

As you begin to read *Chicken Soup for the Chiropractic Soul* we hope that you will be inspired and moved by the heart warming stories of people like yourself who have chosen chiropractic for a holistic approach to healing, pain relief and lifelong wellness. Many of the stories will sound miraculous to you—and to those who experienced them, they were indeed miracles. But once you understand the underlying philosophy of chiropractic, they are really not miraculous at all; they are just the results of the body's innate healing power being released to do its work.

The chiropractic profession has been misunderstood for quite some time as it represents a different viewpoint on health than what is the norm for most. However, there are now millions of people seeking a more conservative, natural and preventative approach as a health choice and chiropractic is leading the field. We hope as you read these stories you will be inspired to experience Chiropractic Care and to share this book with your family, friends and colleagues whom you feel can benefit from this powerful healing art.

When asked why they should create a *Chicken Soup for the Chiropractic Soul*, since millions of books have already been sold in this New York Times Best Selling series, Jack Canfield and Mark Victor Hansen said, "Because both of us and our families have benefited greatly from chiropractic care and we would like to help create a greater awareness as to why chiropractic should be considered as an important part of everyone's health care choice. We hope it will become the greatest communication tool ever created to bring the message of chiropractic to the hundreds of millions of people that can be helped by chiropractic care."

Share with Us

We would love to hear your reactions to the stories in this book. Please let us know what your favorite stories were and how they affected you.

We also invite you to send us stories you would like to see published in future editions of *Chicken Soup for the Soul*.

www.chickensoup.com
Chicken Soup for the Soul
P.O. Box 30880
Santa Barbara, CA 93130
fax: 805-563-2945

You can also submit your Chiropractic stories and comments to *www.chickensoup.parkerseminars.com*.

Also, if you would like to order additional copies of this book please go to *www.chickensoup.parkerseminars.com* or call (866) 333-SOUP.

We hope you enjoy reading this book as much as we enjoyed compiling, editing and writing it.

Dear Reader,

   Due to patient/doctor confidentiality, many subject names have been changed throughout this book to protect the privacy of patients. They are noted with an asterisk(*).

1

OPTIMIZING PEAK PERFORMANCE

The doctor of the future will give no medicine but will interest his patients in the care of the human frame. In diet and in the cause and prevention of disease.

Thomas Edison

Joy and Redemption

True greatness consists in being great in little things.

Charles Simmons

I have gone from the depths of despair and failure to the pinnacle of athletic and personal victory. It's been a long, sometimes anguishing and much-publicized journey. Through it all, one thing is absolutely certain—if not for chiropractic, I would not have won the gold!

In 1989, when I was in my senior year of college at the University of Idaho, and competing at a national level in the decathlon, I began having horrible back pain. I would wake up in the morning and hardly be able to get out of bed. I could stand up straight and I could bend straight over, but anything in-between was excruciating—it shot shocking, grabbing pain into my lower back and down through my hips. I went to the doctor, and he looked me over grimly. The doctor said, "You have two choices— you can either live with the pain, or you can quit."

Quitting was not an option. I had worked and trained too long, and there was too much riding on my potential for me to give up. But it was brutally evident that I could not continue living with the kind of pain I was in. So, I went to see a chiropractor down in Lewiston, Idaho. After two or three treatments, to my delight and surprise, the pain went away. I had almost no symptoms. Sure, I'd wake up in the morning every now and then with some stiffness, but that was it. I went for treatment a half dozen times, things felt fine, and I figured I was good to go. My rationale then was: "If it isn't broken, don't fix it."

I trained hard for the next few years, and then I developed what felt like a really serious pulled groin in 1993. I had zinging pain all the way up into my abdomen, too. My medical doctors could not figure out the problem—it was a mystery to everybody. Finally, I decided to go back to what had worked before: a chiropractor. Suffice it to say that I was out of alignment!

I started getting regular chiropractic maintenance, and from that point on, there probably weren't two weeks that went by where I did not have an adjustment. That's how much it helped. I decided then not just to employ chiropractic care as a way of dealing with symptoms, but to make it an integral part of my training regimen. What chiropractic care gave me, more than anything else I have applied or integrated, is a much better awareness of my body. I started to understand and feel what was going on in my body—I knew when I needed an adjustment, and I began to develop total trust with my chiropractors. They knew my body so well, they could adjust me in the dark.

I ended up taking chiropractic from a method of pain relief to a huge factor in enhancing my performance. Chiropractic care became a part of my lifestyle. It remains a part of my lifestyle to this day, and always will.

I can honestly say, in the last five years, it has remarkably improved my overall wellness. I almost never get sick, and

I don't get headaches. Chiropractic helps in injury prevention and dramatically improves recovery—which is crucial, because I've found that the body cannot heal itself if it's not in alignment.

Two significant moments stand out in my mind that underscore the performance-enhancing qualities of chiropractic. In 1998, I went to the Goodwill Games in New York with my chiropractor from Phoenix, Bob Xanthos. There, after a two-year layoff, I would face the best from around the world. On the first day, during the shot-put, I reared back and let the sixteen-pound ball fly. I felt a nasty tweak in my hips, a real grabber. Intense pain shot down through my hip and into my leg. I was devastated and feared that defending my World Champion status was in serious jeopardy. You are allowed just one medical advisor with you "in the competition," and I had chosen Bob. He adjusted me right there on the field, literally moments before my next event. I high jumped seven feet that day, turning back the best in the world, and went on to win the Goodwill Games.

The highlight of my athletic career came two years before at the 1996 Olympic Games in Atlanta. At that time, I was fortunate enough to have found, through the extensive chiropractic network (the CLA), Rich Gorman from Eugene, Oregon. I knew Rich from the Prefontaine meets. He had a reputation for his fantastic work with elite runners, and since we were both from Oregon, I felt a kinship. He was at the Atlanta Games working with other world-class athletes, so I went and saw him nearly every single day of the week prior to my Olympic competition.

As the competition loomed, I knew I had some demons to exorcise. In 1992, four long, troubling years before, I had failed to make my opening height in the pole vault and lost at the Olympic Trials in New Orleans. At the time, I was the number-one ranked decathlete in the world, was heavily favored to win the gold, and I was part of a massive Reebok media campaign: "Who is the World's Greatest Athlete—Dan or Dave? To Be Settled in Barcelona..." Unfortunately, I couldn't be on the track to settle that score—I was forced to watch from the sidelines as a commentator for NBC. It was pretty tough to take watching Dave, who had never defeated me, wearing that gold medal around his neck.

At the Atlanta Olympic Games, I wasn't about to let that happen again. As prepared as I had ever been physically and mentally, completely aligned from my work with Rich Gorman, I took to the track entirely in tune with my body's every nuance and fluctuation. I felt like a high-performance race car that had undergone total maintenance, and now it was race day. There was complete freedom and unrestricted movement, fluidity I had never experienced before. My legs, hips and torso all flowing in unison. The huge crowd made me nervous, but I had total confidence in my body's ability to perform, to endure what I would put it through for the next two days.

When I stepped up to throw the javelin for the ninth event, I held a slight 150-point lead over the second-place competitor. On my third and final attempt, needing my best throw, I started the rally clap to get myself and the crowd pumped. As the clapping echoed through the stadium, I charged down the runway and hurled the javelin, exploding with my loudest yell ever. The spear seemed to fly forever in the dark summer night, and when it stuck in the turf the crowd erupted and my score flashed on the big screen: 219 feet. My personal best. I had put even more points between second place and myself. I raised my arms in triumph, knowing at that moment that I only needed to survive one last event: the grueling 1,500-meter run, and my Olympic dream would be realized.

Later that night, I stood on the podium a champion.

The American flag rose and waved to the cheers of the packed stadium, and tears of joy and redemption ran down my cheeks as they hung that elusive gold medal, that Holy Grail, around my neck.

Dan O'Brien
As told to Buddy Levy

The Baseball Story

All motion is cyclic. It circulates to the limits of its possibilities and then returns to its starting point.

Robert Collier

I had played baseball my whole life. Little League, junior high, high school, American Legion—you name it, I played it. As it is with many little boys, I had always dreamed of being on the mound with the "big boys." Right after high school, my dream came true. The California Angels drafted me in the third round. I couldn't believe it! Me, Jeffrey D. Conner, the little boy with the big dream, was going to the pros! All those years of practicing and playing, of dreaming and fantasizing, were all about to become reality.

What a thrill it was to be out there on the mound pitching to players I had followed throughout my teenage years. I was in heaven. I'd been pitching for three years when it happened—every pitcher's worst fear—a shoulder injury. The pain was tremendous.

The team doctor sent me to see an orthopedist. After

an examination, I was diagnosed with tendonitis in the shoulder. He prescribed anti-inflammatory medication. I was to take it for ten days and sit out games and practice. After ten days of rest and medication, the pain was still there. I was given another ten days' worth of medicine. Ten more days of no playing. The pain persisted. Back to the doctor. After another examination, he told me there was nothing wrong. His diagnosis: The pain in my shoulder was all in my head. So I finished the season, pitching in pain.

During the off-season, I heard a chiropractor talking on the radio about shoulder injuries. I decided to give it a try. After examining me, the chiropractor discovered I had injured my deltoid muscle and the biceps tendon under the deltoid. The tendon kept popping out of its groove. He adjusted my shoulder, put the tendon back in place and gave me a series of exercises to strengthen my shoulder muscles.

Pain free, I pitched for seven more years. I had a great time during the ten years I spent living my lifelong dream. Now, at age twenty-eight, my baseball career had come to an end, although not through injury. My arm was healthy, but for me, baseball was over. I had to decide what I was going to do with the rest of my life. One day, while reminiscing over the glorious days I had spent in baseball, I remembered how my career had been saved by that chiropractor and how he had helped me continue living my dream. It suddenly hit me. I knew what I wanted to do with my life. I wanted to help people, especially athletes, the way I had been helped. I wanted to be a doctor of chiropractic.

Obtaining my chiropractor's license was just as thrilling as pitching that first ball all those years ago in the pros. I was starting another dream, a dream of helping people. During my career as a chiropractor, I have helped many patients through chiropractic care. However, there is one patient who truly touched my heart.

She was a little girl of four. For two years, every time she rode in a car she got carsick. Every single time. Her parents carried a bucket in the car. They had sought help from numerous doctors and tried every available kind of medication. Nothing worked. Out of desperation, they made an appointment with me.

One of my patients had been talking to them about trying chiropractic care. The parents had no concept of what chiropractic care was all about, but for the sake of their daughter, they decided to try one more doctor.

After the first adjustment, the little girl was able to ride in the car twice before she got sick. The parents were amazed. So they brought her back. After the second adjustment, she went three weeks without getting sick. After the third adjustment, three months with no car-sickness; fourth adjustment, six months with no carsick-ness. And after the fifth adjustment, no more carsickness, period. Every time I help a patient, it gives me a great deal of personal satisfaction.

One of my greatest thrills is the opportunity to treat high school athletes—without charge. One of my patients is a pitcher for his high school team. Professional baseball scouts are following him. His future looks very promising. He has a chance to follow his dream of pitch-ing for the pros.

They say life is a circle. One event leads to another. I was a pitcher, and chiropractic helped save me. Now, I have a chance to give back as I have received—a healthy body and a chance to fulfill dreams.

Jeffrey D. Conner, D.C.
As told to Dawn Planty

[AUTHOR'S NOTE: *That high school pitcher was drafted by the Milwaukee Brewers. Who knows where his dreams will take him?*]

©*Hilary B. Price. Reprinted with Special Permission of* King Features Syndicate.

To Finish What He Started

It was a warm summer day in June in Southern California. The chiropractic volunteer crew for the California AIDS Ride worked from dusk to dawn to see to it that the cyclists would be well taken care of. Being one of the members of this crew, I quickly learned the definition of "benevolence," for it was one of the most loving, giving weeks of my life . . . and the most labor-intensive! The cyclists journeyed on their bicycles from San Francisco to Malibu, California; a total of 575 miles in only seven days. Just to enter the ride, each rider had to raise a minimum of $2,700, all of which went to fight for a cure for HIV. Day six of the seven-day excursion will be a day that will forever linger in my heart.

The day started out overcast, as it usually is on a June morning in Santa Barbara, California. The crew was up at dawn, the chiropractic tables were loaded onto the bus, along with the medical, physical therapy and massage equipment. By day six, our lunch-crew team had a system of teamwork and organization that was working well for us. But today, there was an addition to our crew as one of the riders had injured himself and volunteered to help us. I'll call this rider "Michael."

Michael had decided to help the chiropractic crew since there were only two of us and we were in dire need of an assistant; someone to help with intake forms and taking vital signs. Michael was very willing to pitch in, and I must add on his behalf that he was the best chiropractic assistant I have ever had! We worked for four hours straight without a break. Finally there was a moment to stop and take a break and I asked Michael why he wasn't riding that day. He stated that he "was done for the rest of the ride." "O.K." I replied, "but why aren't you riding anymore?" Michael proceeded to tell me that he has had pain between his shoulder blades for several months now and he has been faithfully seeing a chiropractor for his problem for the past few months. He said he really liked her, however, she could not adjust his spine where he was in pain. He had seen two chiropractors before her, and they too, could not adjust his painful area. Michael was not upset that nobody could adjust him, he was upset that he could not ride in with the rest of the cyclists on day seven of the event. Closing ceremonies would be a very emotional, triumphant time for the riders. Michael wanted to be a part of that. I could see it in his eyes.

The day progressed and we continued to adjust the riders during their lunch break until the last one had arrived. By then we were all exhausted and Michael mentioned how it was harder to be a crew member than a rider. We laughed at his comment, yet none of us denied it either. Then I looked at him and said, "Get on my table, I've got time for one more." I love a good challenge, and Michael had intrigued me with his upper back problem.

"No, no," he replied, "even my own chiropractor can't adjust me, and she's been a chiropractor forever."

This only fueled my fire. "Get on my table!!" This time my voice was a bit more stern, and as a result, Michael willingly obliged. I knew I could adjust Michael's upper back. I had been doing it all week for everybody else, why should he be any different? What came to follow was tear-provoking.

After he felt the adjustment he had been craving for so long, Michael sprung up off my table and got to his knees and hugged my legs and said, "Thank you." He had tears in his eyes. "No one has been able to do that for me."

I told him to get up, that it was no big deal. But to him it was everything.

A few minutes later he was dialing his wife on his cell phone to tell her what had just occurred. He was elated! Now, he would be able to ride in on day seven because he no longer had unbearable back pain. Michael's eyes were dancing as he joyfully helped us pack up our tables and equipment for the day.

Day seven arrived all too soon. Just when we were all settled into our routines and getting to know each other quite well, it was time for our week to end. The emotion present at the closing ceremonies was phenomenal. All our hearts were connected, and although some would not admit it at the time, we were all going to miss that week of kindness and giving. It was a world we all enjoyed, one where love and peace and hard work all prevailed. As a tribute to the volunteer crew members, all 700 riders held up their bicycles as we, the crew, ran by them.

I'll never forget the only rider I got a good glimpse of as I ran by. It was Michael. He was blowing me a kiss as he mouthed the words "thank-you" to me. At that point the tears rolled down my face so quickly that the rest of the riders were a blur. It was then that I understood why he was on his knees the day before, thanking me.

And therein lies the gift of true giving—one man's success, one man's ability to finish what he started.

Caroline Reno, D.C.

A Special Gift

Life is like nothing, because it is everything.

William Golding

My first meeting with A. Lorren Roberts was at the request of Debby, his lovely wife. She had been a patient of mine for several years, and as the manager of the medical supply store, we had gotten to know one another quite well. Her initial conversation was about Lorren, prior to their marriage. He had been an officer in the Vietnam War and, he had been captured by the North Vietnamese Army, tortured, shot, had his leg blown off and all of his fingers broken while submerged under water in a bamboo cage.

He was the first Vietnam Vet I had met who was willing to talk about "the Conflict in South East Asia." Lorren would answer questions candidly as I cautiously asked him about his experience in "Nam." Debby had asked me if I would be able to take care of Lorren, given his history and my reply was simply, "Of course, bring all the medical records you have available and we'll go from there."

Lorren accompanied Debby on her next visit to

"observe" what I did to her. A very tall man, he sat silently, sternly watching my every move with Debby. When her adjustment was finished I walked over to say hello and shake his hand. No smile, no expression, just a hand shake and, "What in the hell are you going to do for me?"

Briefly, I explained the benefits of chiropractic and asked if he would allow me to look at his records and x-rays. He agreed and returned the next day with a stack of over 100 x-rays and at least as many pages of medical records. I explained I would need time to review everything as I performed a Chiropractic exam and took a set of spinal x-rays.

Meanwhile, I learned that before going to Vietnam he had attended college to become an orthopedic surgeon and was very knowledgeable of the musculoskeletal system. He was concerned about shrapnel near his spine and wondered if we would be able to adjust him without causing any further problems. His history also included transient osteomylitis, an infection of the bone that travels around, agent orange exposure, as well as a form of cancer.

Following an extensive review of his records, it was determined that we would begin Chiropractic care. The pre-adjustment evaluation was challenging to say the least. His prosthesis—"Woody," as Lorren called it—was continually shifting at a different angle or falling off, making it impossible to do a proper leg check.

Nevertheless, I started adjusting his spine on his following visit. Several weeks passed while he was getting adjusted three times a week. Lorren didn't mention much about improvement in any condition or symptom and I didn't go into great detail to ask. After all, he understood I wasn't treating any one of his conditions, rather I was correcting any interference in his nervous system, thereby allowing his body to express its full, innate potential.

Finally, Lorren told me he wanted to attempt to play

golf again. He explained that he was a very good golfer, and up until a couple of years ago, played every week. He added that the State Amputee Golf Tournament was coming up and he'd like to participate.

I wasn't sure how Lorren would participate since he was still having difficulty standing, but I encouraged him to go for it. Lorren not only played in the state tournament, he won it! On his next visit he brought me a gift—a gold key-ring he had won at the tournament. I thanked him, congratulated him and proceeded to adjust him.

"By the way," Lorren said, "I am now qualified for the Regional Championship in Myrtle Beach next month. Do you think I should go?"

My reply of course was, "By all means, go. Have a good time."

The next month passed and I hadn't really given much thought to the tournament. "Wish me luck," Lorren said as he left one afternoon. "Tomorrow I'm off to Myrtle Beach."

The phone call the following week was unexpected, however welcomed. It was Lorren with great news, "Doc, I won! I won! I can't wait to see you tomorrow."

On his next visit, Lorren stumbled into the adjusting room with so much excitement that "Woody" came loose and he nearly fell onto the adjusting table. After I checked his spine and made some "tune-ups" he came off the table with a glow in his eyes and smile on his face.

"Doc," he said, "you have given me something no other doctor could, the VA couldn't and none of the medics, surgeries or therapy were able to do. You see, not only am I back on the golf course, not only am I playing the best golf of my life, not only am I winning tournaments, but I have something back I never told you about! I am able to make love to my wife again for the first time in several years. There is no price I can put on that. I want you to have this." Lorren handed me a silver medallion of some kind with two pins on it. I wasn't sure what to say. "You don't know what this is, do you?" he asked. "Those are the wings I earned in Vietnam. They belong to you now, and I want you to have them."

Joel Miller, D.C.

Chiropractic Got Me
to the Boston Marathon

Welcome every problem as an opportunity.
Each moment is the greatest challenge, the best
thing that ever happened to you.
The more difficult the problem, the greater the
challenge in working it out.

                                                    Grace Speare

I'm a competitive amateur athlete, serious about my
training but far from world class. For many years I participated in about eight to twelve triathlons a season, rang-
ing from the short sprint races to longer Olympic-style
distances. I did well in each race, usually placed in the top-
ten women overall, enjoyed the variety of training, but
never felt like I could do any better or could go any further. Just as many athletes do, I maintained a training log-
book each year, constantly recording every workout,
every day, every week.

One February, I decided to take a year off from
triathlons and tackle the marathon. Though it was my

second time running a full marathon, my goal was simply to run fast enough to qualify for the Boston Marathon, which was my ultimate goal. This meant running in less than three hours, forty minutes, which meant an average of less than eight thirty per mile, not an easy task for twenty-six straight miles.

At the same time, I started going to a chiropractor because I was suffering from headaches. I was in the corporate world, working long hours and always stressed-out. After only a few adjustments, I was amazed at how much better I felt in such a short time. I was even more amazed at what the doctor told me and how excited he was when telling me about chiropractic. It made so much sense to me. I, too, became very excited about chiropractic.

Well, many months passed by. I continued to get regular chiropractic adjustments and continued to train for the marathon, running up to fifty miles per week. October approached and I went to Washington, D.C. to run in the Marine Corps Marathon. My hard work paid off as I finished in three thirty seven, which qualified me for the Boston Marathon the next year. I was so excited—I had reached my goal.

About a month later, I pulled out my training log from the previous year, a year in which I participated in many triathlons. I noticed that after every single race I ran, I had to take off two, and often three days of training because I was sick! Right there in my book, it said Monday — off/sick; Tuesday—off/sick; Wednesday—off/sick. What was going on? This was a pattern! I know triathlons are physically stressful, but that was crazy. I wasn't able to continue my workouts after all those races because I was getting sick. My immune system must not have been that strong.

Then I reviewed my training log from the current year, the year I started my marathon training and the year I started chiropractic care. I looked through every month, week by week, and noticed that I did not take one single day off from training because I was sick. Not one. Sure, I took a day off to rest my body, but I never took a day off because I was sick. I was just simply never sick! I stayed healthy! My immune system was strong!

It was at that moment that I realized the power of chiropractic. Chiropractic is what helped me run that marathon and achieve my goal. Though I was the one who forced myself out the door to run five days a week, who went to the track every Tuesday night to do speed work, who made myself run 15-20 miles on a single Saturday morning, I realized it was chiropractic that enabled me to stay healthy enough so that I was able to perform at that level on a consistent basis.

Chiropractic kept me healthy, kept me energized, kept me injury free and kept me subluxation free. I was the one who made me run, but it was chiropractic that allowed my body to be healthy enough that it could successfully handle the stress of training hard for a marathon. Sure, if I hadn't had the discipline I may not have qualified, but chiropractic allowed me to get there.

Five months after this realization, I ran the Boston Marathon. Five months after the Boston Marathon, I left my job, moved to Atlanta, and began Chiropractic College. It made that much difference in my life. I am now able to give that reward back to others who come into my office every day.

Pamela Stone, D.C.

A Daring Adventure

For as long as I can remember, my husband Warne and I had longed to hike the entire length of the legendary Appalachian Trail. The wilderness romanticism, the rugged individualism, the intrigue of a self-sufficient 2000 mile journey on foot; it was an untamed frontier in our own backyard. He even proposed to me on a jagged alpine summit on a day-hike amidst reindeer lichen, bare granite, and near gale-force winds on the fabled Appalachian Trail.

Life's pleasantries and plans, however, had been violently interrupted for years by my perpetual, excruciating migraines. Oppressive daily painkillers and industrial-strength migraine drugs kept me zonked out enough not to care. My cherished work in the Shenandoah's deep forests and sky-kissed ridges was a haze, and physical activity a determined struggle.

On one sun-baked August traverse, I was plodding along in a miserable medicinal fog when Warne, a highly experienced backpacker, disappointedly confided that he didn't think I'd ever be able to hike the Appalachian Trail. I just couldn't undertake a journey of that magnitude. Utter devastation didn't even begin to describe how I felt. One of our most treasured dreams had died.

I nearly gave up when my neurologist insisted that my blood pressure, skyrocketing from the mind-numbing medication, be controlled with yet more high dosage prescriptions. Instead, in the dead of winter, despite hopelessness and fear, I gathered up my nerve and abandoned dreams, defiantly taking the first step of a daring new adventure. Nervously lacing up my comfortable old trail boots, I fussed with the well-worn grommets, wondering whether I really had the strength to do this. After all, I was deliberately running from conventional authority to a less-traveled path. Taking one last look around, I opened the door and intrepidly set off on my search, a quest for the life-changing wisdom of an acupuncturist.

In silence, I sat on the little carpeted bench as Dr. Berman, who was also a chiropractor, diagnosed a seriously pinched nerve on the x-ray, which he could treat to lower my dangerous blood pressure and eliminate the blinding headaches. I desperately wanted to believe him, but I'd learned not to get my hopes up. Decades of doctors and neurologists had only scarcely eased the nightmarish, knife-in-the-eye migraines. I figured it would be two weeks, tops, if he was really good, before the next headache floored me. Even so, I began making regular trips to his office for chiropractic and acupuncture treatments. Two weeks came and went—no pain, no migraines. In fact, I'm still waiting. The next one never did appear.

The skillful chiropractic adjustments, and non-piercing acupuncture was so mild and non-invasive that I wondered how it could possibly help. But, slowly my neck stabilized, blood pressure dropped and I got off the addictive medication.

The holistic treatment took me much further on my journey than I had ever expected to travel. For years, on the backcountry hikes I lead, I'd also been tormented by a searing tree-pollen allergy, foot bones painfully out of line, and worn knee cartilage that made steep descents agoniz-ingly slow. The effects of the acupunture needles and the absolute relief of gentle spinal manipulations yielded con-sistent and progressive healing by eliminating the causes rather than drugging the symptoms.

Finally set free of persistent pain, heavy medication, and hasty side effects, active recreation became fun again. Warne was amazed at how happy and unstressed I'd become—how effortlessly I climbed the craggy, cloud-bound peaks.

On Valentine's Day we talked of dreams, of hiking the high peaks, and of the ever-compelling Appalachian Trail. Then he handed me to the essential topographical maps for the Long Trail; the long-recognized, classic training ground in Vermont for preparing to hike the Appalachian Trail.

Never in my wildest imagination did I suspect my dreams would be returned through the hands of a chiro-practor and acupuncture. We're planning daring adven-tures that stir the soul because they're really possible now. It's not just about restoring health; it's about restoring dreams.

Gloria Updyke

$\overline{2}$

MIRACLES

*We do not need more intellectual power,
we need more spiritual power. . .
We do not need more of the things that are
seen, we need more of the things that are
unseen.*

Calvin Coolidge

Vertigo

Kathy Ibey had turned her head with unexpected results one fateful day about three and a half years before she entered my office. I say fateful because it was almost exactly the same time that I was graduating from chiropractic college. Although our lives didn't cross for three and one half years, our paths did cross in a special way on one memorable Christmas Eve.

Kathy had merely turned her head to view something behind her, and the world began to spin and never stopped, not even when she slept. Kathy went to her primary care physician and received referral after referral until one day she was referred to the leading neurologist in the state.

The diagnosis was insidious onset vertigo, and no treatment to her eyes, ears, nose or throat helped her. MRIs of her head revealed no abnormalities. The medical doctors were in a quandary about the cause of, and cure for, Kathy's problem, which had only gotten worse over a three-year period. Kathy never had a moment of relief from the spinning. She had to sleep in an upright position, otherwise the spinning became even more intense.

One of the leading neurologists in the state instructed

her to sit in the middle of her couch and thrust herself from side to side to create a vigorous jarring effect as she smashed into the sides of the couch.

Her close friend, Janice, who claimed that I performed miracles, referred Kathy to my office. Kathy felt she needed a miracle since all of her previous doctors had failed and no one gave her any hope or direction. So as a last resort, Kathy took Janice's advice and went to a chiropractor. Unbeknownst to her, chiropractic would be her miracle.

Kathy was practically carried into my office by her husband. She could not stand or walk unassisted and had been unable to move without assistance since the onset of her condition.

Kathy's history was one of the more extensive I had ever taken. A physical exam and x-ray revealed a problem in the upper part of her neck. As I explained the unique relationship of the top bone on the spine—the atlas—to the head, Kathy's face and eyes began to show the hope that had been gone for so long.

Kathy received adjustments three times a week for a couple of months, and her condition improved slightly. She could lie down to sleep but was still unable to function on her own. She was beginning to lose a sense of her self-worth and self-respect. I prayed, pondered and meditated that I might find an answer to solve this peculiar condition, which I had not previously seen to this extreme in my experience as a doctor.

After three months of regular treatments with good responsive adjustments to the upper neck, Kathy still showed only slight improvement. I began to wonder if I could help this dear lady. I began to have brief moments of not doubt, but perplexity. Should I refer her to another doctor, a specialist in weird and uncommon conditions? Then I realized that it was to me that people sent individuals with those conditions. So I prayed, pondered, meditated and studied some more. In my studies I came across some information on vertigo related to the sinuses, inner ear, and the temporomandibular joint (TMJ), or the jaw joint. Although all of her inner ear and sinus tests and x-rays were negative, I had a good feeling about this research.

On Christmas Eve we were preparing to close the office early so we could spend time with our families, and Kathy was my last patient. I explained what procedure I would be doing and what I expected to happen. I anticipated an increase in sinus drainage and a release of pressure on the inner ear, thus creating an equalization of pressure from inner ear to outer ear, a return to balance, and relief from the vertigo. I performed the TMJ maneuver, and instantly, before I could raise the adjusting table, Kathy began to gag and choke on the sinus drainage. She said it was as if someone had turned on a faucet and fluid started running down her throat. I instructed her to spit it out into the wastebasket.

Kathy's husband ran to get her a glass of water as she sat at the waste basket spitting for several minutes, asking between spits, "How much fluid is in there?"

I said, "I don't know, but get as much out as possible."

After about ten minutes of spitting, Kathy stood up and walked down a thirty-foot hallway unassisted with a glass of water in her hand. When she reached the end of the hallway, she turned around and said, "Come on. We need to start therapy so Dr. Holland can get home to his children."

Kathy's husband and I stood outside the adjustment room watching in wonder at this lady, who for the past three years could not take an unassisted step and now could walk thirty feet with such ease and balance without spilling a drop of water from her cup. Mr. Ibey and I began to cry. Kathy noticed our tears and realized what she had done.

Kathy has continued to receive treatment in my office. Within six weeks of this fateful Christmas Eve, she was able to drive herself to my office for the first time in over three years.

John Holland, D.C.

The One Who Walked Away!
The Miracle Man

On a crisp, beautiful March morning, I went to my airplane hanger, pulled back the door, and prepared my
Cessna 172 for a pleasure flight—a flight that would
change my life forever. For me, a successful businessman
with a beautiful and loving wife and all the things I'd
worked hard to achieve, that morning was like any other
as I prepared my plane for takeoff. After a careful pre-flight
check, my wheels left the ground and I was free from the
earth below and soaring like an eagle. The scenery below
was breathtaking—rivers and inlets, trees and fields, and
the vast Atlantic Ocean hidden from the mainland by
seven beautiful barrier islands. After flying for an hour, I
turned for home. As I prepared to land, everything was
going smoothly as I decreased my speed to the mandatory
75 mph, required because of the short, 1,300-foot runway.
I was well above the power and electric lines that all air-
planes avoided on descent.

Without warning, my engine lost power and the Cessna
started dropping to the ground. Hitting some high tension
wires my plane was whipped to the ground, crashing

head first and upside down. The next thing I remember
was the mangled metal that was once my airplane, while
the paramedics worked on my broken body. A deep voice
was telling me that I must return—that there was still
work left for me to do on earth. Before I could reply, I
found myself going through a long, pitch-black tunnel,
and back again, in a pain-ravaged body. As they pulled my
virtually lifeless body from the wreckage, my rescuers
knew there was not much chance of survival. The ambulance raced to the hospital. There was a lot to be done in a
very short time just to save my life. As the teams of doctors swarmed over my mangled body at the hospital, my
family was given the bleak news.

My neck was broken at the first and second cervical vertebrae and my spinal cord was crushed. My swallowing
reflex was destroyed and I did not have the ability to eat or
drink. My diaphragm was destroyed, so breathing on my
own was lost. My family was told I would never breathe
without the use of a respirator. My jaw was crushed and
almost every bone in my face and skull was broken. My
bowel, bladder and kidneys did not function. The nerves
that control my heartbeat, respiration, and blood pressure
were damaged. Almost every muscle in my body was damaged and I did not have voluntary control of a single
muscle except for my eyelids. I could blink my eyes. For a
long time that was the only way I communicated with the
outside world—one blink for yes, and two for no.

The most hope the doctors offered was that I might one
day sit in a wheelchair and blink my eyes. With all this in
mind, I began to formulate a plan for victory. I prayed to
God for the strength and courage I would need for the
long, hard battle. I would tackle this one step at a time. My
secret motto became "a cinch by the inch." James Allen
once stated, "You're presently where your thoughts take
you."

None of us fully realize the awesome power of the human mind. Scientists tell us outer space is the last frontier, but I disagree. I think the human mind is the last frontier. I planned on using this marvelous power-center almighty God endowed us with to recover and walk out of the hospital as a normal man.

First I had to find a way to communicate. My sister developed a system that enabled me to do this using my eyelids. My next challenge was to be free of the respirator and to breathe on my own.

While laying in bed one night a thought kept flashing in my mind over and over—breathe deep, breathe deep. I took one hundred deep breaths with the aid of the respirator. Every breath brought excruciating pain. Despite the pain, I rested five minutes and took one hundred more. I was not to be denied. My entire body was racked with pain but I hung on; one minute at a time. A large clock hung on the wall at the foot of my bed. The pain was so severe I would just set the goal to make it through one minute. I would watch the second hand go around. A minute seemed like an eternity. Then I would say to myself, *Okay Morris, you made it one minute, let's go for two.* My persistence would pay off months later. I gradually increased my breathing program to where I would take three hundred breaths with the respirator, rest five minutes, and take three hundred more. But still I could not take one breath on my own.

I didn't give up. And then one night all my prayers and hard work were rewarded. I took three hundred deep breaths and rested. Suddenly I breathed on my own three times. A few days later the respiratory therapy team reduced the mechanical breathing assistance to 90%, leaving me to breathe unassisted 10% of the time. Over the following weeks the assistance was reduce to 80/20 and then to 70/30, until finally, it was removed and I was breathing completely unassisted! The doctors learned I had built-up my stomach muscles enough to replace the need for my diaphragm. This had never been done before!

My next goal was learning to talk. After hundreds of hours of speech therapy, I finally learned to say two words—"no" and "mama." And then more words, and finally sentences.

My third major challenge was the ability to eat on my own and freedom from the feeding machine. I'll never forget the day that goal was reached. What a joy it was to be able to eat on my own.

My final major challenge was learning to walk. When I told the doctors I planned on walking out of the hospital on my own two feet they just laughed. "Why don't you be realistic," they said. But I thought of them as "dream stealers" and attacked my therapy like a man possessed. I arranged for the orderlies to wake me up at five-thirty so I could be in therapy by seven-thirty—an hour and a half before everyone else arrived. They would wheel me up to the parallel bars and I would struggle to stand up. Day after day the fight to walk moved me to action, and miraculously I walked out of the hospital on my own five months later! They were difficult steps, but I did it. I was a changed man, determined to keep fighting and trusting.

After leaving the hospital, the doctors told me that I should be satisfied with the way I was and that even though there are limitations in the wheelchair, I should be happy that I was alive. One day I was reviewing documents with my business partner who told me about a doctor of chiropractic. Although I was unfamiliar with chiropractic, I decided to schedule a consultation with Dr. Jack Kenley. He and I sat and talked for about an hour. He seemed to be actually concerned. He had a positive attitude and he said he could help me. We created a relationship that has lasted to this day—I saw him every day for the next five years! I've made giant leaps because of him. I believe my rehabilitation would have been spent in a wheelchair, as the doctors thought, if it wasn't for chiropractic! In fact, I describe Dr. Jack Kenley as the most caring and dedicated physician I have ever known . . . and believe me I've known many in my days!

Morris Goodman
as told to Donald K. Kase

The Miracle

At age sixteen, George James woke up one morning to discover that he had lost the vision in his right eye. Shocked and dismayed at this sudden loss, his mother immediately made arrangements for him to be examined at Wills Eye Hospital in Philadelphia. After extensive testing, the doctors announced that they could not find the reason for his loss of sight. For an entire year, George continued to return for follow-up exams hoping the doctors would find the cause of his problem. Later, he consulted a neurosurgeon who suggested that he might be suffering from multiple sclerosis which could account for his visual disturbance. Finally, George was referred to another renowned eye specialist in Philadelphia. Again, exhaustive testing and examination procedures were undertaken. The doctor had to honestly and regretfully inform George that there was no known medical reason for his loss of vision.

Discouraged, George feared a life of disability and gradual deterioration from his suspected multiple sclerosis. For some twelve years longer, he lived with his problem, always expecting the worst.

Then, he woke up one morning with a severe headache

and terrible neck pain. "Aspirins wouldn't even begin to touch it," he said. A very close friend suggested that he make an appointment with me. She felt sure that chiropractic could help George with his headaches and neck pains.

George was skeptical, never having considered this type of treatment before. The pain continued and George finally consented to give this new doctor a try. After all, what did he have to lose? Things couldn't get much worse! George called for his first appointment.

After a careful case history and examination, his spine was x-rayed to determine the possibility of spinal nerve pressure. The films confirmed the presence of serious vertebral misalignments that were apparently causing his headaches and neck pains. After his first corrective spinal adjustment, George began to experience some relief. The next evening was when the "miracle" occurred! George was watching television when his right eye "flashed with sight for about a half hour." It then faded away once again. Puzzled and frightened, George didn't tell anyone at first. The next day his vision returned again, and stayed, getting clearer and stronger.

George visited me two days later and not only reported the improvement in his head and neck pain, but also the return of vision in his right eye. I was almost speechless, I covered his good eye and gave him a brochure to read, which he did without difficulty. I gave him another one at random and he was able to read that one as well. George had a comprehensive eye examination several weeks later that showed the visual acuity in his right eye to be 20/30, almost normal. His vision returned to normal and remains that way.

Richard L. Hartman, D.C.

The Battle Within a Man

The Vietnam War is what brought Ed to our office. From the moment that he walked through the door, I could see that the war hadn't really ended. I could still see it raging in Ed's eyes.

The day I first talked to Ed, he was on the other end of the phone, and I was wondering what help chiropractic could possibly offer this man. He told me of his life, which hardly seemed like living. He could barely walk, hadn't sat down in years and couldn't remember the last time that he had slept for longer than two to three hours. Still new to the chiropractic profession, I felt emptiness in my heart because I feared that there was no help for this man.

Day One arrived and Ed was over an hour early for his appointment. A ghost of a man walked through the door, and we all took a minute to catch our breath. Ed came to the front desk and introduced himself. I explained that I would help him fill out his paperwork, but he had to let me know where he would be most comfortable. In the blink of an eye he was on the floor on his knees: "This is the only position that I have." As we continued, it became evident that this man's life had been stolen by an unmerciful thief: his war injury.

On November 14, 1969, Ed Kerestesy was shot in the back of his left leg. His hamstring was blasted apart, as was his life. For eight months, Ed lay in a hospital bed pumped full of morphine. He received a skin graft before his release but was never instructed to seek further care once he returned home. He was left with the task of getting used to his new body and beginning life again. Back on American soil in 1970, Ed used crutches and wore a brace because the substantial injury to his hamstring had left him with what the medics diagnosed as 'drop foot'. Ed then decided to help himself because he had been told no one else could help him. He placed weights on his bent left leg to try to curb the drop foot and stop the leg from bending in order to help him walk. The weights worked to straighten the leg, but the results were hardly enough to satisfy a man who wanted his life back. By bending his leg back, his body became twisted and he had difficulty with movement and sitting on his buttocks. One day, he woke up to realize that he could no longer sit; his contorted frame would not allow for it. Furthermore, he began to experience excruciating lower back pain, intense burning hip pain, arm numbness, constant fatigue, loss of appetite, joint pain and stiffness, continued leg pain and difficulty walking.

Thus began Ed's personal battle. In 1970, he began working in the mines because a man could work on his knees and no one would question him. At night, he lay on the couch with one leg hanging over the back, but he did not sleep.

When he was lucky, he could escape the constant pain for a few short hours each night and experience a most unpeaceful sleep.

When the mines closed in 1982, Ed was left without a livelihood because there was no work for a bent man who could only remain productive while crouched on his knees. Thus began the years of family turmoil, anger, mental anguish, exacerbated physical pain and solitude. Ed never left his house because he didn't want pity and didn't know where to go for help.

Thankfully, after eight years of confinement in his house, Ed found something that he could do—play pool. Bending over a pool table can be rather easy for a man who is already bent. This is where Ed originally found his hope. Ed told a story at the pool hall of how, while walking through Sears, he had caught a glimpse of himself on a TV monitor and didn't recognize the man he saw. His eyes were sunken with dark circles beneath them, and his body was twisted and bent. The image terrified him. A patient from our clinic was there and told Ed about the wonderful results she and her husband had experienced while under chiropractic care. She convinced Ed to give chiropractic a chance. What did he really have to lose? At that moment he didn't have anything worth losing.

Before me sat a man with little hope and fewer expectations. I may have been just as skeptical because I began to feel his hopelessness. But chiropractic care is hope, and there was definitely hope for Ed.

Dr. Fanella took Ed into his office and sat on the floor across from him. If Ed was comfortable on his knees, then that was where the doctor needed to be. When it came time for the actual adjustment, Ed became apprehensive. Lying flat caused him a great deal of pain. So the doctor remedied that by adjusting Ed while he sat on his knees.

Ed walked to the waiting room and dropped to his knees. His back went into spasms and he had no control over it. The next day he called to ask what was happening to him. He felt like a zombie. He could barely hold his eyes open, and his family had to help him move his body. He was near sleep at all times—couldn't talk but could hear everything around him. His body was healing. This went on for weeks. Ed would come in to get adjusted and return home to sleep.

Just as suddenly as it was brought about, Ed's healing time of constant fatigue lifted. Immediately, he could sit on his buttocks. He stood taller, his leg pain decreased and he began to sleep the entire night through. The results just kept getting better. Ed walked in one Monday morning a few months after beginning care to exclaim, "Guess what I did this weekend!" Ed had driven to Ohio to see his daughter. He had sat on his buttocks and driven a car for three straight hours, and, most important, did so with no pain!

Most mornings, Ed walks through our door and looks excited. Ed is thrilled because he now has things to look forward to. He is always working—making up for lost time. Ed enjoys the simple things that had been missing from his life for thirty years, like walking.

For thirty years Ed was angry and pained, but all that has changed now. "The most profound change is my state of mind because I am actually happy now," he says.

Sarah Dixon-Emerick

Do You Believe in Miracles?

In the fall of 1997, after a year and a half of many visits to different specialists and many, many, tests, I was told that I would probably never conceive; and at thirty-one years of age I was labeled infertile. This was a devastating diagnosis for two people who really wanted children.

In April 1998, my first visit to Dr. Hardick was prompted by a stiff neck. Dr. Hardick first took some x-rays of my spine and neck. He was quite concerned about the x-ray results, as I had a severe subluxation in my lower back. He explained to me that this vertebrae housed the nerve endings that supported organs in my body such as my bladder, bowel and reproductive organs. As we were looking at the x-rays, Dr. Hardick asked if my husband and I had any children. I then explained to him my clinical diagnosis of being infertile.

Dr. Hardick asked me to give him three months and explained that he wasn't God, but he would do what he could to help me. I started a very disciplined schedule of appointments with Dr. Hardick, and almost immediately noticed that, in general, I felt better. When I ran at the gym, my legs no longer ached. I tried to put out of my mind what Dr. Hardick had told me—because I didn't

want to get my hopes up too high—but at night I would
pray for God to work through Dr. Hardick's hands and
bless us with the gift of a child.

On August 18, 1998, my husband and I found out that
we were six weeks pregnant. There are absolutely no
words to describe how I felt that day! The doctors were
amazed—all but Dr. Hardick. He wasn't surprised at all.
He simply smiled and said, "I thought chiropractic could
help you."

Annette Klosler

[AUTHOR'S NOTE: *Lauren Nicole was born in May 1999 and
contiunues to bring so much joy to our lives. She truly is a little
angel from above and a miracle of life and love.*]

Return to Sanity

My patient, Jim, worked as an orderly in a mental institution. Jim's job included calming down and restraining difficult and sometimes violent patients. He usually got the upper hand, but sometimes the inmates won. He'd come in for an adjustment all scratched up, bitten and subluxated.

"A sucker punch Doc. I didn't see it coming. She really surprised me."

But he did more than fight inmates. He also took more manageable patients out for walks and drives.

One evening, Jim appeared for his appointment with a tall, good-looking and very wary eighteen-year-old.

"Hi Jim, who's your friend?" I asked.

"This is Larry. He's an inmate. He was committed about eight months ago by his family. He's been diagnosed as paranoid schizophrenic—hears voices. His condition hasn't improved and he's on lots of meds (medications).

"Want to give Larry an adjustment?"

Larry let me palpate his neck and even agreed to lie on his side for an upper cervical adjustment. His atlas was out. I positioned the drop headpiece and set it up on his neck. *I probably won't get another chance to do this,* I thought to myself.

The headpiece dropped down and Larry jumped up. It looked like he went from a lying position to a standing one with no intermediate positions. "What did you do to me?" he yelled.

"I, uh, I adjusted your atlas, it was out." Not my finest patient lecture.

"It felt like you stuck a sword through my head," said Larry.

I turned to Craig for some kind of help but he was doubled up in laughter. "Funniest thing I've ever seen. You should see your face Dr. Tedd."

Eventually he came up and put his arm around Larry. "Hey, he does this to me all the time. Let's go get some pizza. See you in a couple of days doc."

They drove away. I never saw Larry again.

Jim came in two days later, "How's Larry?" were the first words out of my mouth.

"Oh yeah, I meant to call you doc. They've cut back Larry's meds. He suddenly seems better. The psychiatrists are convinced the drugs finally started working," Jim laughed.

Jim came by the next week with more news, "Larry was taken off all meds today. The voices have stopped, and his family is coming in tomorrow to bring him home."

"He's back to normal? No more strange behavior?" I asked.

"Well, there's just one thing that's upsetting the staff."

"What's that?"

"He keeps telling people he wants to be a chiropractor."

Tedd Koren, D.C.

"Gloria I would appricate it if you would stop greeting the patients with 'Welcome to the Crack House!'"

CLOSE TO HOME. ©*John McPherson. Reprinted with permission of UNIVERSAL PRESS SYNDICATE. All rights reserved.*

In-Flight Adjustment

I had been in practice for about ninety days when I heard over the airplane intercom, "Is there a doctor on the plane? Flight 14793 is experiencing a medical emergency. If there is a physician on the plane, we need you to identify yourself immediately."

I sat there in my seat thinking, *Wow, I sure hope there is a doctor on this plane.*

After a few minutes they made the next announcement. "We're having a medical emergency and we're urgently requesting any physician or nurse on the plane to identify themselves." They started going down the totem pole.

I knew that if they were calling for a doctor on a plane, it was something serious; someone was having a seizure or a stroke, a woman was giving birth, or someone was having a heart attack.

I started to think of my Chiropractic career as an intern in Chiropractic College. *How could I help?* I finally got the courage to push the call button. The stewardess came running down and asked me to follow her.

So I walked with her up to the front of the plane and she asked, "What kind of doctor?" (silence.) I was embarrassed to tell her I was a chiropractor. I finally mumbled, "I'm a chiropractor" (mumbled.) She replied, and I'm not making this up, "Is that a real doctor?"

She walked me up to the very front of the plane, and there was the pilot, convulsing on the floor of the cockpit. So I sat next to the man, grabbed his head and started to palpate.

I let the co-pilot know that I was going to adjust the pilot's neck and that he might hear a popping sound. Then I adjusted him. In ten seconds, his eyes dropped back in his head and he stopped flailing all around. He came right out of his convulsion, and he looked at me and said, "Who the hell are you?"

Three weeks later I got a call from the pilot. He told me, "Dr. Singer, I want you to know they found a tumor in the top of my head. They said it was compressing all the arteries and veins in my brain; there was no oxygen. The doctors said it's a miracle that I survived. I don't know what you did . . . and I talked to all the people in the cockpit and they said you took my neck and did something you called an adjustment. Well, that adjustment saved my life and I want to know if you can adjust me again."

David Singer, D.C.

7

The Power That Made
the Body Heals the Body

As a competitive swimmer for the University of
Wisconsin, I was traveling the country as one of the tops
in my field. While training midway through my first year,
I began to lose sensation to my left arm from the shoulder
to my finger tips. Upon further examination, I also lost a
pulse to that arm. I could not use a screwdriver or a tooth-
brush with that hand. The medical doctors diagnosed
shoulder problems. They placed me on fifteen different
anti-inflammatory drugs, and, as each one wore off, I
received a new prescription. This was destroying my liver,
kidneys and digestive and immune system which made
me chronically ill.

This continued until I was given a product that we now
know causes cancer and is only used on racehorses. Since
anti-inflammatory drugs only mask the problem, I continued to train and further damage my body. Because I
wasn't getting any better, and in fact was getting worse,
the university hospital began to run tests on me. They
gave me every poke, prod and scan. I was the guinea pig,
with up to twelve residents gawking at a time. No one

could believe what was happening in my body.

Following about $20,000 worth of testing, I was told that I needed to have a rib taken out to make room for the nerves, arteries and veins. I spent the next year and a half in search of a second opinion that differed from the first. I saw the best specialists in the country only to be told the same thing at each office. While searching for a solution other than surgery, I lost my swimming scholarship, lost my ability to study, and lost friends and family due to my attempts to squelch my depression with alcohol.

I lost everything I had worked for over the last twelve years. I then decided to have the surgery as there seemed no other recourse. It did not work. So I continued my downward spiral and could have killed myself, or someone else, by drunk driving seven nights a week.

Then, when the bottom fell out, someone recommended that I try chiropractic. While skeptical, I listened to Dr. Beyler and it made so much sense. I knew I was in a special place from the beginning. Within the first couple of adjustments he was able to temporarily restore the blood and nerve flow to my left arm. From then on, I knew what I would do for the rest of my life. I would be a Chiropractor committed to saving others lives just as I am convinced Dr. Beyler saved mine.

Mark David Lagerkvist, D.C.

Faith in Chiropractic

It's the constant and determined effort that breaks down all resistance, sweeps away all obstacles.

Claude M. Bristol

Mrs. Mitchell was sitting in a wheelchair. A large woman, with an afghan across her legs down to her feet, she gruffly dismissed her assistant and said, "I want you to fix this." At which point she took away the afghan to reveal swollen, inflamed feet with pus oozing from her toenails and her feet blackened all the way up and over her ankles.

Well, my positive attitude faded as much as the color in my face as I looked at this poor woman's condition. I think I said something like, "Uh, I think you're in the wrong place, lady. You should be in a hospital."

She stared me down and said, "No, I've been to the hospital already and they can't help me. They only want to amputate." Then she took my hand and said in a somewhat softer tone, "I know you can help me, I have faith in you."

What is this, I thought? *This woman, a complete stranger with gangrene almost up to her knees tells me she has faith in me to help her? Well, she has more faith than I have!* Then it hit me . . . she has faith in chiropractic, not me.

Well, we talked some more and I tried to dissuade her some more and before you knew it, she had talked me into trying to do something to help. No; not help, cure!

After a short but futile attempt at chiropractic philosophy (you've got to understand this doesn't come under the practice of chiropractic) I finally wrote up some silly form of disclaimer saying that she insisted despite my protests to the contrary, blah, blah, and that she didn't hold me responsible. For what? If she died? And she probably would, the poor soul. She signed and we started.

Well, first we got a three-view set of x-rays of her neck then somehow got her down onto the adjusting table for an adjustment. She was told to come back in a couple of days and was adjusted again. This went on for about a month.

She kept encouraging me as we went along, and one day we thought we saw some pink where there was once only black! Yes, folks, I'm here to tell you that as time went on, she continued to improve. The last time I saw Mrs. Mitchell, after about four or five months of further care, she walked into the office said she was "okay now," and didn't think she needed any more adjustments. Oh yes, she thanked me and told me that she just knew I could help her.

Gil Ramirez, D.C.

Restored Faith

Glenn was a hardworking, dedicated high school teacher. I met him at a local city festival. He told me that his right arm felt "dead." It had gradually become numb from his armpit to the tips of his fingers. He had, over the previous nineteen months, consulted with his family physician, three neurologists, an orthopedist, a physical therapist and a hand specialist. The testing had been extensive including a CT scan, MRI, NCV, EMG, x-rays and a discogram. The results were inconclusive. He labored through rehabilitative exercises, multiple pre-scriptions, and physical therapy and was currently in the midst of psychotheraphy sessions because the most recent diagnosis for his "dead arm" was that of a psycho-somatic disorder.

He desperately accepted my offer of a free consultation to explore chiropractic options and began chiropractic care in February. His x-rays revealed considerable verte-bral subluxation in his lower neck. Ironically, his previous x-ray report had a one-word conclusion, "Normal." I adjusted him frequently at the onset of his care program and then tapered off slightly as better movement returned to his neck.

I got to know Glenn quite well over the next few months. To this day, I don't think I've ever met a more giving, gentle spirit than his. He greeted me at every visit with a smile that naturally brightened the entire room. I looked forward to his visits because he always seemed to have a tidbit of wisdom to impart upon my practice. I adjusted patients in an open area with six tables near each other and often times I'd find him conversing and sharing his experiences with the people on the tables nearest his.

I grew more and more saddened, however, when each visit revealed the same news, "There is no change to my 'dead' arm." Over the first few months, I continued to encourage him and assure him as I worked diligently to free the compressed nerve in his neck. He knew he would be better off without the subluxations in his neck, but both of us still agonized that his arm remained dead.

Twenty visits passed; thirty, forty . . . no change. He remained the most positive, optimistic person I had known, but I was growing weary. I second-guessed my technique, my diagnosis, and my efforts.

Approximately seven months and nearly sixty visits had passed. He continued to report no change. It was a September afternoon when my receptionist informed me that Glenn was waiting for me in a consultation room. Since this was not normal, I was concerned that something was most definitely wrong and I suspected that he may be giving up. My heart sank when I entered the room and found my strong, steady and gentle friend sobbing deeply with his face buried in his hands. Quickly reaching him I put my hand on his forearm and asked what was wrong. With swollen, red eyes Glenn said, "I didn't want to tell you on my last visit because I didn't think it was real, but my arm . . .it's alive!" He continued, "My hand still remains numb but my arm is back to normal. I'm almost afraid to believe it."

We celebrated that day and a new zeal returned to my adjustments. Over the next few months it became a source of anticipated excitement to see how the life was slowly returning to his hand. He began to feel his palm, then his fingers, and eventually his thumb. Today he has full function of his arm and hand. The only residual damage he currently experiences is a numb spot about the size of a marble on his right thumbnail. His thumbnail now serves as an inspiration to other patients of mine as his story has been passed along. As for Glenn, I still look forward to his visits. He greets me from across the room with a loud, "Get over here, Doc, and adjust my thumbnail!" His faith has restored mine and for that I am eternally grateful.

Jeffrey W. Danielson, D.C.

Can You Turn It Back Off?

The wife of one of my patients dropped in and asked to speak to me. It was obvious she was distraught. She began by saying that she did not even know why she had come to see me. When I asked her to tell me about it, she told me that she had just come from her doctor's office and that he had told her she was pregnant. I offered my congratulations.

"Dr. Watson, you don't understand. My husband is sterile. We gave up trying to have a baby twelve years ago when Jim's urologist told him that he would never father a child."

"Now I know why you've come to see me. Do you remember during Jim's original consultation when I specifically asked him if he had any bowel, urinary or sexual dysfunctions problems? He told me he didn't. One of the reasons I asked about sexual dysfunction was to prevent just this kind of situation. When the nerves to the reproduction system are blocked it can cause sterility. When the spinal column is adjusted back into alignment and the organs receive the proper nerve supply, these kinds of healings can occur."

She rolled her eyes and said, "He'll never believe that!"

I asked that she come in with him the next day so I could talk to them together.

When they arrived I had them sent to my office instead of the adjusting room. I told him, "I have good news and good news, or bad news and bad news, or any combination, depending on how you look at it."

"What's up?" Jim asked.

"Do you remember me asking you if you had any bowel, urinary or sexual dysfunction problems?"

"Yes, I remember, and I told you I didn't."

I told him that I had been told since then that he was sterile and he agreed that he was. I told him, "'Was' is correct. You *were*, but you aren't *now*. You are now *fertile*."

"What do you mean?" he asked.

"You were sterile because of a pinched nerve between your brain and your reproductive organs. As I adjusted your low back so your back problem could begin to heal, I evidently removed the pinch on that nerve too." He could not take it in, so I said, "You are no longer sterile. You are fertile and your wife is pregnant."

"What are you talking about?" he asked.

"Jim," I said, "listen to me. You are no longer sterile and your wife is going to have a baby. You are going to be a father."

Jim looked at his wife and back to me. Then he looked back to her and a thought started to form in his mind as he looked back to me. I stuck my finger to his nose and said, "Don't you even think about it."

His wife said, "Jim, honey, my doctor says I am pregnant and I think I am. I have been faithful to you. You are this baby's daddy," she began to cry, "or his name is going to be Jesus."

I suggested that he give her the benefit of the doubt and compare baby pictures. He agreed to do that. The baby was a boy and looked enough like his daddy's baby pictures to have been him.

About five years later, Jim came in to see me. He said, "Doc, we now have four children. Can you turn it back off for me?"

John Watson, D.C.

ChiroTOONS by Peter Cranton

Farmer Brown's suspicions were confirmed . . .
#23 had gotten out to see
the new Chiropractor down the lane.

Reprinted by permission of Peter Cranton.

3

SAY GOODBYE TO PAIN

As to disease, make a habit of two things—to help, or at least to do no harm.

Hippocrates

Turning Nightmares Into Dreams

When I was five years old, I began to experience headaches. The headaches would begin innocently enough with a dull, nagging sort of pain that seemed more of an annoyance than anything. However, this annoyance would quickly escalate into an excruciating torment nearly beyond description. The headache usually drove me home after school to my bedroom where the blinds would come down and I would lie in the dark—motionless—praying that somehow the pain would disappear. But of course it never would.

After a usual bout of nausea and vomiting, I would eventually drift off to sleep while listening to the joyful sounds and delights of the neighborhood kids playing outside; something I never seemed to be able to join. If luck was on my side, I would sleep until morning and then just wait for the whole process to start all over again the next day.

Medications barely touched the pain, ice or heat didn't do a thing, nor did massages or reassurance from Mom and Dad. I was trapped in a body that seemed to rebel against me at every given opportunity. As a five-year-old, I had to greatly alter what should have been a carefree life in order to deal with the debilitating and limiting pain. My parents felt incredibly helpless, as I am sure most parents would. What parent wouldn't trade places with their child and assume the position of pain if they could? However, wishes and hopes, as I soon learned, don't always come true. So my parents began to seek medical help and took me to see the family physician. This doctor sent me to the pharmacy, prescription in hand. When I found no relief, a second trip to the doctor earned me a pass to the physical therapist. When only a little relief followed, a second family physician was sought.

This visit yielded to an appointment with a specialist, a neurologist for the first time. An allergist followed the neurologist, who pondered the negative results of more than one thousand allergy tests. Next an ear, eyes, nose and throat specialist was consulted who decided that the best route would be with another neurologist. I was subjected to a CAT scan, a test to study the structure of the brain. Then an MRI was ordered, another picture of the brain structure. These tests finally led me to the office of a psychiatrist, because when medicine had no answers, it certainly must have just been in my mind. However, this avenue of treatment just landed me at the same junction as the other treatments: a dead end.

Everyone made an attempt at diagnosis and treatment. Everyone tried to solve the problems of a five-year-old child that seemed to have no solution. A suffering five-year-old turned six, a fourth-grader entered the fifth grade, and a child became a teenager. Each passing year brought more approaches to diagnosis, more theories, more specialists and more false hopes. Sadly, for ten years, no one could help me.

What began as an annoying headache had slowly become an endless, hopeless process that, beginning at age five, had lasted double a child's known painless life. A happy childhood was now an empty, hollow existence in which self-esteem was destroyed, a smile was lost, and a life was stolen.

However, one very vital aspect of health care had been overlooked, and when I was fifteen years old, holistic medicine and I crossed paths. A chiropractor moved to town and began a practice. As one last shot at finding a normal life for their son, my parents took me to see the young practitioner. After a very careful workup and thorough explanation of chiropractic care, we started adjustments and treatment. I faithfully attended three times per week and followed this regime for four weeks. It quickly became custom that at the start of each visit, the chiropractor walked into the room and asked the same question, "How is the headache today?"

Patience was a virtue that I had been forced to learn during the ten years of enduring my condition. I had learned to tolerate the same endless questions, the same empty answers, and the same frustrating results. However, one month later, it was the answer to one question that changed my life. It was the twelfth time that the doctor posed the interrogating words, "How is the headache today?" For the first time in ten years, I was able to say, "I don't have one."

In one miraculous month my headaches disappeared. Four weeks of aggressive care resulted in no more pain, no more dark rooms, sad days, dreaded tears, or hopeless suffering.

What had taken everyone else ten years to miss, it took chiropractic one month to find. And it found my life. It found my soul. It found lost years of a child and created amazing potential of a young man. And it was at the end of that month that, at age fifteen, I decided to dedicate my life to the practice of chiropractic. I wished to acquire the amazing secret, to hold the passion, and to be able to execute the knowledge, ability, and power of holding such a simple gift in my hands.

Six years later, I found myself attending my first day of chiropractic school. Four years after that I entered my first day in practice as a chiropractic doctor. I finally understood that the most important journeys in life may not always be the easiest ones. Perhaps the years of painful endurance as a child had led me to years of wonderful rewards as an adult and a doctor.

About six months into my first year of practice, I had a patient walk into my office and tell me through tears that I was her last hope. Mary was an attractive lady in her late forties who had suffered from migraine headaches since early adulthood. When asked what was the longest period she had ever gone without experiencing a headache, her silence spoke volumes: She had not gone more than two days without a headache in over twenty years. In the back of my mind, I could still feel a child's pounding head in a dark room and I prayed that I would be able to help this woman.

We began a treatment plan, and although it was hard, Mary stuck with it and trusted me and my decisions. Two months later I was shocked when I entered the room and once again found Mary in tears. Fearful that I had not met her expectations, I sat quietly beside her hoping the right apologetic words would come to me to tell her I was not able to achieve what she had hoped. However, before I could get one word out she took my hand and whispered, "They're gone. For the first time since I can remember, my headaches are gone. I wish you could know what it's like."

I smiled and replied, "Mary, I do."

A child's painful nightmare had in fact shown the path to a young adult's dream.

Dr. Kyle C. Kelbert

Journey to Freedom from Pain

Curled up in the fetal position in silence on my bedroom floor, I would lie in self-imposed darkness while pleading with God to end my miserable existence.

The excruciating pain that accompanied my all too frequent migraine headaches had once again crippled me to the point where death would have been a welcome relief.

At the age of fifty and after enduring for more than twenty years, the debilitating effects that migraine headaches inflicted on my body, relief from my agony was closer that I could have ever imagined.

I suffered from a long list of physical ailments that began almost as soon as I entered the world. When I was only nine months old, I was diagnosed with polio. As a result, I now experience Post-Polio Syndrome. Those conditions brought about the early stages of osteoarthritis and fibromyalgia. I battled bursitis and tendonitis throughout my body, and have arthritis in every major weight-bearing joint.

In an effort to ease my pain, doctors performed no fewer than forty-two surgeries and numerous other medical procedures on my ravaged body. All have been met with little to no success. To say that I live in chronic pain would be a woeful understatement.

Death would have been better than anything else at that point. I was having up to three migraines a month, with each lasting up to three and a half days.

Migraines can be triggered by many things including high stress levels, food allergies, simple headaches, hormone irregularities, and nutritional imbalances such as low blood sugar levels. The pain can be both physically and mentally debilitating. In addition, sufferers may experience extreme sensitivity to both light and sound.

I ran through all the common remedies from over the counter medications such as Tylenol and Motrin, to prescription drugs such as Relafin and Imitrex. Nothing provided the relief I sought, including the Imitrex, which was designed specifically for migraine sufferers.

Imitrex comes in a shot. The first time they gave me one, the doctors showed me how to do it. I sat on my bed for almost fifteen minutes getting up the courage to do it and debated whether the pain was worse than giving myself the shot. Within ten minutes of taking the injection, I went into a dizzy episode. I literally felt the room begin to spin from the reaction. I'd fall asleep for about two hours. Sometimes I'd wake up with the headache still there and go through the whole process again. It didn't eliminate the headache, but it took enough of the edge off that I could at least walk around the house. But I was still light and sound sensitive.

The migraines kept me from enjoying many of the things most take for granted. My son couldn't have friends over because I couldn't stand the sound. If the dog barked, I would just freak out. My husband had to take our son to all of his sporting events because they were outdoors in sunlight. I'd miss almost all of the school trips because I was curled up in a dark room somewhere trying to deal with the pain.

It wasn't until 1998 when I saw a glimmer of hope. A dear friend of mine was referred to a wonderful doctor. She found out that chiropractic care was effective in treating headaches and insisted that I go see him. She had seen my suffering and actually drove me to my first appointment.

I was nervous about my first trip to the chiropractor's office. The idea of getting my back "cracked" was not appealing, but with the thoughts of the pain inflicted by my migraines still fresh in my mind, I was willing to give chiropractic a chance.

On my first visit, I knew something was different. As the doctor began the consultation, he seemed to actually care about my health condition. I'm not saying that medical doctors didn't, it was just different.

Of the seventeen different conditions that I listed on my medical history chart, the doctor gave me the option of which I would like treated first. Without hesitation, it was the migraines.

He asked many questions about the history of my migraines. Questions like when they started and the relationship between eating, not eating, smells, perfumes, stress, emotions, childhood illness, and so on. He listened. He didn't just shake his head and write another prescription.

During the consultation, the doctor explained what a subluxation was and the resulting effects that it places on the spine. A thorough examination ensued, and when the doctor reached the muscles of the shoulders and neck, I could feel the pain radiate up into my head.

When he began to touch the muscles and joints in my neck and shoulders, I felt the pain go up the back of my neck and into my head. I was amazed that headaches could come from the neck and shoulders. In all of my years of going to medical doctors, none of them even suggested that they could be contributors to my migraines.

With no guarantees of relief, only the hope that the doctor was on to something bigger, I underwent two weeks of daily treatments. It was determined that the years of physical stress on my body, and compensating for my disabilities, caused my body to be imbalanced.

During the next nine months, I had one migraine. At the onset of symptoms, I went to the doctor's office and the pain subsided within hours. Over the last three years, I have had only two bouts with migraines.

Today, with the help of regular chiropractic care, I believe that my chronic pain has been cut in half, but that can't begin to measure against the personal joy it has brought me.

My relief from migraines came at a time when my son was in the final years of high school. To see the joy on his face when I was able to attend his sporting events was priceless. He didn't care if he won or lost, he only cared that I was there.

Cheryl Girnus
As told to Frank A. Corbo, D.C.

A Family Affair

I grew up in a typical small town surrounded by the love of my family. When I entered high school I began experiencing headaches, often so severe I could not function, let alone sit in class. I recall my visits to the school nurse's office and the comments they made to my mother, like, "She's just trying to get out of school and the headaches are the excuse." Fortunately my mother knew that complaining wasn't part of my personality.

My search for relief from my headaches continued by seeing my family doctor. Unfortunately, he was unable to locate the source of my headaches, and so began a long journey with pain pills. All I wanted to do was cope with the pain.

After high school and into marriage, my severe headaches continued. By this time I was taking pain medication on almost an hourly basis. But instead of getting better, the headaches began to worsen. All they could do was push more medicine in me to numb the pain. It got to the point where I would be totally incapacitated, not able to function normally. The Vicodin, combined with over-the-counter medication, helped take the edge off the pain, but it knocked me out. Because of that, and because when I had migraines I was in bed throwing up, some-times for a couple of days, I had to plan everything around whether I had a headache. During the six years I suffered from these massive headaches, I couldn't count the times my husband had to take me to the hospital for a shot of Demorol. The pain would subside, but I'd sleep the entire weekend.

Many worried that I was becoming addicted to painkillers. But I wasn't addicted to the medicine, I was addicted to the fact that I didn't want to have severe headaches.

Between chronic pain and just plain frustration with no end in sight, I started seriously searching for a cure. I was determined to fight for a normal life and I began reading, researching, and learning what was going on with my body. From one doctor to the next I heard the same thing—there's not much else we can do. I felt like a pinball bouncing from one specialist to another. I was examined by all kinds of medical doctors, neurologists, even eye doctors. But I still had no answers. One of the doctors referred me to an allergist. I began a course of allergy shots two to three times a week. But in the end, the story was the same—he could not get me off the pain medicine. However, he did refer me to a dentist to be tested for a TMJ problem.

It was this referral that put me on the right track. The dentist confirmed the diagnosis of temporomandibular joint disfunction (TMJD), and fitted me for braces in the hope of returning my jaw to its normal position. The brac-ing provided some relief, but not enough to satisfy my dentist or me. My dentist recommended that I see a chiro-practor, as he believed I might have a muscular problem as well.

Feeling that a cure was in sight I agreed. I had never been to a doctor of chiropractic before, and did not know what the benefits were, but I made the appointment out of sheer determination. The day of the appointment I was so sick with a migraine that I couldn't get out of bed. I called to cancel the appointment, but the chiropractor explained that this was the perfect opportunity to find the reasons for my migraines. I reluctantly agreed.

I dragged myself into the car and drove to the appointment. I vomited in the bathroom before seeing the doctor. The first thing the chiropractor did was search for the trigger to my headaches. Pressing on different spots, the doctor felt for the trigger of the pain. I remember him pressing dozens of muscles and asking each time if I felt pain. When he pressed above my jaw, I immediately began to vomit. With a calm and concerned voice, the chiropractor said, "I believe we have found the problem."

With every visit my pain diminished. My need for constant medication disappeared. The change in my life was incredible. I no longer had to plan my life around my headaches. After seeing the change in my life and my recovery for himself, my husband started seeing my chiropractor because of an accident. My boys, Adam and Aaron, have gone to him for care of baseball injuries, too.

My whole family has seen first-hand the change in my life. They've experienced the frustration and the relief right along with me. The feeling of helplessness that your family goes through is hard to put into words, and I'm so thankful for them. Today, we are back to living and the painful years of searching for answers are behind us. To finally understand what it was that took away so many years of my life, and then to find relief, is one of the greatest blessings I could ever receive.

Linda Randall
As told to Dr. Frank A. Corbo

ChiroTOONS by Peter Cranton

". . . I now pronounce you husband and wife,
you may adjust the bride."

Reprinted by permission of Peter Cranton.

Life Is Great

His name is Robert*—Rob for short. He seemed as ordinary a new patient as any I had ever encountered in my "lengthy" three-year career. The only unusual feature about Rob was the silver dollar-sized bruise perfectly centered in the middle of his forehead.

The patient history form indicated his primary (and only) complaint as migraines, which Rob softly described as "real skullbusters." "They come and go," he said. Rob's very intelligently related history detailed years of suffering. "They have been more frequent in recent years. They have also become much more intense. When I have them, they're debilitating. I have to go into a darkened room and lie motionless for hours, sometimes even for days. I can't work. My boss told me that if I miss any more work I will lose my job."

I tried to remain calm and confident while Rob continued to describe endless encounters with health care personnel of every type. "I have had every test there is," he said. "I have tried every type of drug there is. Nothing has worked. The drugs sometimes reduce the pain, but it is still unbearable; and I vomit a lot." I pointed at the bruise on Rob's forehead and asked, "Is that what I think it is?"

"That depends on what you think it is," came his immediate reply. "I think your headaches are so bad that you ram your head against a wall to override the headache pain," I responded.

Rob was not impressed with my recollecting something I had read a handful of years earlier about the behaviors of severe migraine sufferers. "Yes," Rob responded, rather flatly. "I don't do it often, but a couple of days ago I had one of the worst skullbusters I've had in a while. I couldn't take it anymore."

I had come to realize that Rob's face was the definition of a man in pain. His eyes were those of a tortured man. His every movement was minimized and performed with painstaking care so as not to aggravate his condition.

I found myself wondering if I would be able to help this poor fellow. Actually I was wondering if anything could help him. It seemed he had tried everything. "Everything except chiropractic," Rob continued. "I've tried many different medical doctors including neurologists, psychiatrists, physiatrists, anesthesiologists. I've tried acupuncture and massage. In total, I've been to fourteen different doctors. I think it only fair to tell you," Rob continued, "if you can't help me, I'm going to slip into something heavy and take a long walk off a short pier. I don't want you to feel any pressure or anything. I just want you to know that if that happens, it's not your fault."

No pressure! How could I not feel pressure?! It had become quite obvious to me that Rob was not a man who was even capable of joking anymore. Years of "skullbusters" had seen to that. He was quite serious. If I couldn't help him find some relief he was going to kill himself!

"Rob," I stammered, searching for words that would provide him with a glimmer of hope, "chiropractic is often very effective at relieving many people of their headaches.

But, chiropractic doesn't work the same for everyone. I can't make any promises, but I can tell you that I am going to work diligently to find if you have a chiropractic problem that can cause a headache, and then I am going to try and fix that problem in the hopes that your headaches will subside, or even go away." Rob weakly nodded that he understood. I felt that I had thoroughly failed at giving him any semblance of hope.

I performed as complete an examination on Rob as I knew how to do. I tried to uncover anything wrong; anything that could be causing his headaches. What I found was not much. Except for a slightly unusual movement pattern in his upper cervical region his physical examination was totally unremarkable. But I couldn't pin it down. Something, small as it was, was just not right. "There's only one way to further find out what is really going on in your upper neck," I told Rob. "I need to take a few x-rays of the region. Then I can better see what is going on in there."

I continued with the usual explanation about how many headaches are caused by problems in the neck, and chiropractic treatment of the neck can work towards correcting such problems. Rob seemed to show a slight flicker of hope, or did I just want him to so badly that I imagined it. Anyway, he told me that no one had taken any x-rays of his neck before so we might as well give it a try.

Within fifteen minutes or so, I had a few x-rays of Rob's neck. I did my usual swift analysis the first time through. I was sure I would quickly find the large alien that I knew must certainly be holding a jackhammer to one of Rob's cervical vertebrae or the inside of his skull. Nothing. Rob sat quietly in the dimly lit room with me, watching me scan his x-rays mounted on the view box. I began analyzing the x-rays for a second time—this time much more slowly.

Well, that can't be, I thought to myself. During my second perusal of Rob's x-rays I noticed that his atlas, the very top bone of the spine, the one upon which the head rests, was rotated out of its normal alignment by an incredible degree. I thought, *He should have been crippled or dead with a vertebra that far out of whack!*

Rob was no dummy. A computer genius, Rob had brains; even if they were screaming in pain most of the time. He could tell I saw something. "Do you see anything?" He sounded almost hopeful.

"Yes. The top bone in your neck is rotated—a lot." I continued with a pretty in-depth explanation of cervical anatomy, describing blood vessels and nerves, using "the crimping of a garden hose" example. "But you see," I continued, "this is rotated much more than I have ever seen or even heard of." I tried to sound encouraged that we might have found a cause of his pain, while trying not to sound too alarmed at the excessive nature of what I found.

Rob had only one question—"Can you help me?"

"Rob, in chiropractic, we adjust bones that are out of alignment, like this one, and adjust them back into place; kind of like an orthodontist who gently moves teeth into proper alignment."

Rob only wanted to know one thing, "Will this get rid of my headaches?"

"I don't know," I responded, hating myself for being honest. "It should. I would think that it will provide you with some relief. But to be honest, there's no way to know for sure."

"When can we start putting this bone back in place?" Rob asked. If he wasn't hurting so badly from his latest "skullbuster," I think he would have actually been excited. "We can begin today," I optimistically responded. And with that, I explained my treatment protocol and began treating Rob.

Now, I would like to brag that Rob was pain-free after the first treatment. I even would have been thrilled to say that Rob responded rapidly after just a few treatments. But to be honest, Rob's response was slow. He improved incrementally with nearly every treatment. He related that his headaches were diminishing, both in their frequency and intensity. Rob's face, in fact his very demeanor, changed. At first he began smiling; then joking. He even gained a couple of pounds (he says because he was not just "renting" his food anymore, as he had been before when his migraines made him vomit).

Rob did not miss any more work. In fact while completing his treatment he related to me that he got a promotion at work, which was soon followed by a new car. The Christmas card he sent me several months after his treatment concluded informed me he had even bought his first home. "Life," he wrote inside the card, "is great. Thanks."

As a doctor of chiropractic, I see a number of different maladies and disorders, but I never see any immediate life-threatening injuries or ailments, as do emergency room physicians or paramedics. On a few occasions I confess to wondering, *What would it be like to* save *a life?* With Rob, I think I know.

The last I heard, Rob was engaged! For Rob, *life* is great.

Michael Kohler, D.C.

A Life Changed Once—and Again

I don't really remember walking without a limp. I don't really remember getting around without a brace. I don't really remember a time when my back didn't hurt, my head didn't ache, or my hips didn't throb at least some of the time.

But there was such a time when I was very little, when I ran freely and would spin around looking at the sky 'til I fell down . . . laughing. I just don't remember it. The history of my leg injury is a history beginning with adventure and ending with a life—changed.

It all began when I ventured out after my brother one day. I was a barefooted toddler without fear. The day was hot and so was the asphalt. It burned my feet badly. After that, there was the emergency room with doctors, medicines and shots. It was a shot in my hip that changed the course of my life. A shot intended to keep down infection was the culprit. That needle from a shot of antibiotics hit my sciatic nerve and damaged my growth forever.

The rest is a history of more hospitals, surgeries, braces and surgeries. The final outcome was always the same; my left leg would always be smaller, shorter and weaker. I would always need a brace to walk. I could never play volleyball, or dance like a ballerina, or run with my children in a field of flowers. I was disabled and there wasn't a thing anyone could do about it. Until now.

Forty years, and a thousand headaches and backaches later, I reluctantly entered Dr. Tom's office. I had seen a chiropractor once, and he hurt me, so I was never going back, until now. I thought to myself, *wasn't it an M.D. who hurt me the first time? I've seen dozens of them since then. Why not give this guy a try?* So there I sat in the office nervously awaiting my turn.

Outwardly, I wasn't hopeful because there had been so many physicians filled with empty promises. I guess I had become used to my aches and pains. I've always had an enormous amount of energy, getting around quite well. So why did I really need to come? I told myself it was to satisfy my husband and my friends, to tell them that I had tried, to no avail. But deep inside I hoped for something.

That was months ago. We started out slowly. There were x-rays and measurements, exercises and therapies. I came almost every day and, little by little, I noticed that my back didn't hurt so much. I didn't get headaches as frequently and I was beginning to walk a little taller and easier.

It was tough at first. Everything hurt. But my family and friends kept encouraging me. Dr. Tom insisted that it was my body reacting to years and years of atrophy. I didn't even realize how uneven my hips were, or that I had never tried to touch my toes or stretch my muscles, or challenge my diagnosis.

Dr. Tom challenged me. At first I wanted to quit, but I am glad that I didn't. I feel better today than I have in, well, since I can remember. Sure I have aches and pains, don't all Baby Boomers? But not like before, never like before. I had once again a life.

Most likely, I will always walk with a brace. My left leg

will be shorter and smaller, but it won't be quite as weak. I won't live with the headaches and backaches like before. I'll continue to get stronger, walk taller and become the best I can be. I'll continue to partner with Dr. Tom. I'll continue to play an active role in my own healing. I'll continue to hope, this time outwardly, for an even better tomorrow. Who knows? Some day I may even tango at my children's weddings. Today, I believe that anything's possible.

Susie Latham
as told to Mary Beth Garrison

$\overline{4}$

PEDIATRICS AND CHIROPRACTIC

Seek not to understand that you may believe,
but believe that you may understand.

Saint Augustine

The Unborn Child

August 1996 was a major milestone in Donovan's and my life. I was pregnant with our first child. It was an uncomplicated pregnancy, especially with the chiropractic treatment Donovan gave me as I gained weight and my spine changed. I was so excited to have this child naturally. Most of the mothers who came into the clinic expressed their misfortunes of childbearing experiences, except Kellie, my sister-in-law. Kellie spoke of the beauty of the experience and the excitement of bringing a child into the world. I hung onto her words, because, like all first time mothers, I was afraid of the unexpected.

One evening while Donovan and I were attending a child birthing class, the instructor stated that out of every three deliveries, one would be a c-section. I had this horrible feeling in my gut that it would be me. I had gone to all of the required prenatal visits and at each visit, everything was okay.

At 4:30 A.M. on May 17, 1997, I said, "Honey, I think my water broke!" Donovan bolted out of bed to get me a towel, and we waited a few minutes. Then he called the doctor and they told us to go to the hospital immediately.

Forty-five minutes later, we arrived at the hospital and made it through admissions smoothly. I was placed in a room and a nurse hooked me up to heart and contraction monitors. While the nurse checked my dilation, Donovan went downstairs to get all our gear. The minute he left, my doctor popped in to check the baby. He didn't like what he felt, so he brought in an ultra sound machine. After one scan he said, "Your child is breech, and you will have to have an emergency cesarean."

I was devastated! I held back my tears as fear took over me. I went through the cesarean successfully and Kellie, our new daughter, was healthy. After carrying my child for nine months, I felt like I missed out on the grand finale of giving birth.

We were so ready to go home, but Kellie had a positive hip test. We were told that her hips were dislocated due to the breech position in which she had been. Three days into Kellie's life, we had to take her to Children's Hospital for the orthopedist to check her. As we waited patiently for two hours, I looked at all of the different children and parents and prayed they would all receive the care they needed. Finally, another doctor came in and confirmed that her hips were bilaterally dislocated. Kellie would have to wear a full-body brace for six months. I could feel my eyes filling up with wet tears as they placed this con-traption on my tiny daughter's body. We rode home quietly. Kellie's legs were pushed out like a frog in this brace that went up above her shoulders, around her back and front, and down her legs to her tiny little feet. The six months slowly passed. Everything from bathing to dia-pering had to be done differently. Even so, she was an amazing little girl. Donovan worked with her legs often, which was a warmth of reassurance to me.

In June 1999, I was pregnant with our second child. I again attended all of the required doctors' appointments and everything was going well until about the eighth month. I was told my child was breech again. I was devastated as a doctor explained the invasive procedure to try and turn the child before birth. I would have to wait until I was thirty-three weeks before they could try to physically turn the baby from the outside of my stomach. The procedure would cause bruising, and sometimes a cesarean delivery would have to take place immediately. The chances of the procedure being successful were fifty percent.

That evening, I explained the news regarding our breech child to Donovan. He immediately reassured me that there was a chiropractic procedure to turn breech babies. However, he had not had the opportunity to use the technique, so he called his brother who he knew had helped a number of pregnant women turn their unborn children.

After three treatments, being adjusted every other day, the baby turned. We were lying in bed, and I felt movement that I had never experienced before. Donovan and I lay holding my stomach as we physically felt our child turn inside. I was so relieved. Donovan's chiropractic care had taken away my disappointments of having another cesarean and the fear of my second child being traumatized by wearing a brace.

On March 22, 1999, at 3:12 A.M., I felt a pain, and my water broke. Forty-five minutes later, we arrived at the hospital. We skipped admissions and two simple pushes later, our second daughter, Kaitlyn, was born naturally without a doctor present. She was immediately laid on my chest for warmth and breastfeeding. After having delivered Kaitlyn, I felt as though my pregnancy was complete and that I had experienced the child birthing process as God had intended.

Because of my wonderful experience with chiropractic, I was able to successfully fulfill a dream and desire to have a child naturally.

Catherine Boykin

Healing Hands

We shall see but a little way if we require to understand what we see.

Henry David Thoreau

I was a senior intern attending patients when an announcement over the intercom brought me to the reception area. Two of my regular patients, Chad and Nancy* looking painfully distraught, were waiting for me. They held their first child, Tommy, only six days old, and asked me if there was anything I could do for their tiny boy. I escorted the family to a private area and asked for any information that would help me make my necessary assessment of the case.

Chad told me that Nancy's labor had been prolonged and with difficulties—the obstetrician had delivered the baby with forceps. From his first moments of life the baby wouldn't nurse or take formula. He then developed esophageal reflux and rejected the tiny amounts that he could manage to swallow, and although he was listless and weak; he was restless and wasn't sleeping. Tommy lost precious weight, becoming weaker by the hour, and then began to hemorrhage internally. Earlier that very morning the doctor diagnosed their son with "failure to thrive," advising them there was nothing more to be done for him. The parents were advised to decide if they wanted to leave him in the hospital or to take him home to die. Chad said, "So, Dennis, we decided to stop at the clinic and ask if there was anything that you thought chiropractic could do for him. It certainly can't hurt him," Chad pleaded.

Tommy's body was tiny and listless, yet restless as I placed him onto my lap. Loudly coursing through my mind were the humbling thoughts; *this is the tiniest patient I've yet experienced. What pressure will be adequate to be corrective, yet not harmful?*

Feeling his neck, I could detect a right subluxation, possibly resulting from the forceps delivery. Making contact with my thumb on the tip of his first vertebrae, I gave a gentle, straight lateral thrust, and felt the segment jump away from my thumb! Tommy gave a sharp, brief cry and all three of us startled at the sound that the strong audible created in the quiet room.

Handing the baby to his father, I told them to take him home and see how he progressed through the day. There was no further chiropractic care I could give him at that time. For the remainder of that afternoon I could hardly think of anything but the life and death struggle in which I had just played a part. So new were my chiropractic skills, over and over questions plagued me. *What if I killed this child? The attending medical doctors all but gave this baby a diagnosis of death. Were the M.D.s right?* The audible "crack" was still loud in my ears as these thoughts continued to churn.

Later that night I received a call from Chad, and hearing his emotion-choked voice, I immediately feared the worst news. My knees went weak as I heard the best of all possible reports; Tommy had taken a bottle (his first meal) without any sign of reflux, and was finally sleeping peace-fully for the first time in his life!

Dennis Downey, DC
As told to Sara Aurora Downey, D.C.

Please Help My Baby

About two years ago I was told a story about a family who had been blessed with their very first baby boy in 1965. This boy was special in the sense that upon his birth, he did not act like the rest of the newborns in the hospital nursery. He was a very quiet baby, never cried, and many times just lay there without normal extemporaneous movement, but yet was alert to his surroundings. The delivering doctor noted this abnormality in the chart but did not inform the parents of the situation since there was no real physical problem. It was his decision to tell the parents that the baby seemed to be very healthy.

Late the next afternoon, the mother, *Jane, excitedly brought the baby, *Timmy, to his new home. Jane noticed right away that Timmy was not like her friend's babies. There was no cooing, crying, or arms and legs flailing. Although Timmy ate regularly, Jane couldn't get over the feeling that there might be something wrong. Mother's intuition.

Upon waking the next morning, Jane found what most mothers would dread seeing; little Timmy was a sickly shade of blue and his little body seemed as though it was gasping for every breath. Jane frantically telephoned the hospital and incoherently informed the doctor that there was something wrong with Timmy. Through her sobbing the doctor was given enough information to understand that it was imperative that Timmy be brought back to the hospital.

Jane rushed the baby into the hospital where the doctor immediately met her. In Jane's distraught state, she silently held out Timmy's frail, blue, gasping body for the doctor to take. The only words she could muster as he took her baby from her were, "Please help my baby." Little Timmy was whisked away to the emergency room.

While Timmy was being looked after in the emergency room, Jane went to the nearest phone knowing that she couldn't go through this ordeal by herself. She wanted to call her husband, but being a truck driver she knew there was no way of reaching him. She knew she wouldn't be able to work through this ordeal alone and hoped that Grace, her mother, would be home to give her some mental and emotional support. Grace answered the phone and Jane emotionally fell apart. Jane explained that Timmy had turned blue and was having trouble breathing. "Mom, I don't know what I'm going to do. He turned a darker blue and had more trouble breathing just in the ride to the hospital." Holding back tears, Grace let Jane know that she would be at the hospital shortly.

Jane slowly hung up the phone and sat in the chair; contemplating what was happening to her and her newborn baby. Many questions streamed through her head. She felt as though she had just entered into the Twilight Zone. She was to find out that this was nothing compared to what was to come.

Grace had just arrived and was hugging Jane as the doctor walked into the waiting room. The doctor had both women sit down. He began by explaining, "We have run some preliminary tests and thus far we are unable to deduce what is causing Timmy's deep blue color other than his body's inability to obtain enough oxygen for normal functioning. According to the test results, there is no reason why Timmy should be gasping for oxygen." Very slowly and methodically Jane asked, "Can you help my baby?"

The doctor continued, "We're doing everything we possibly can. There are some more tests that we can run. We'd like to keep Timmy overnight for observation." Tears began to stream down Jane's face, "So you're telling me you can't help my baby?"

"I feel that if we keep him overnight for observation and more testing, we would be able to understand his condition better. This would afford us the opportunity to decide on a particular therapy. It's imperative that we get more oxygen into his body," the doctor informed the two distraught ladies.

Jane asked if she could see Timmy. The doctor said that wouldn't be a problem. He would have a nurse come and get her when the baby was ready. With that, the doctor left. Jane, sobbing in Grace's arms asked, "What am I going to do, Mom? I feel as if something doesn't happen quickly, Timmy's going to die. I'm scared, Mom. I don't want to lose my baby boy. Please! Isn't there anything we can do to help him?"

Grace lifted Jane's chin and looked into her tear-filled eyes and said, "The doctor has no idea what's going on. Let's take Timmy to the chiropractor."

Although Jane had heard chiropractors referred to as quacks, she was open to anything at this point. Grace explained that the chiropractor, whom she worked for, had really helped a lot of people when medical doctors could not find the cause of the problem. It was up to Jane whether or not Timmy was to go visit the chiropractor.

Both Jane and Grace were finally summoned to the

room where Timmy was. The sight of Timmy's lifeless and very dark blue body with tubes stuck into his little bulbous nose reminded Jane of a baby corpse in a plastic coffin. This image struck Jane so hard that she felt she was going to try her mother's idea and no one was going to stand in her way, not even her apprehension toward chiropractors. What else could she do? Nothing. There were no more available options. With that decision, Jane picked up Timmy's lifeless body, gently removed the oxygen tubes, and whispered to Timmy, "Don't worry; Mommy's going to help you. Mommy loves you, Timmy. She isn't going to let anything bad happen to you." Jane then turned to Grace with assured conviction and said, "Let's go see if your chiropractor can help him!"

Grace and Jane walked down the hallway and just as the elevator door was opening, a nurse started running down the hallway toward them. The nurse yelled, "You can't take him with you! He needs oxygen! Bring him back! He'll die!"

"He'll die if I keep him here!" Jane yelled back, just as the elevator door slammed shut. Jane looked into Timmy's big, dark brown eyes and said, "But Mama's little boy isn't going to die." Jane hugged Timmy tighter as Grace threw her arms around both Jane and Timmy. Both women began to lightly sob as they rode the elevator down to the first floor.

They rushed out to the car and drove over to the chiropractor's office as fast as they could. Upon seeing the dark blue lifeless body, the receptionist told them to go right in. As Grace and Jane barged into the adjusting room, the doctor was just finishing up with a very surprised patient. The doctor immediately saw the reason for the rude entrance. He took Timmy and placed him on the adjusting table while Grace gave the doctor a quick synopsis of their situation. Jane, standing by the door with her arms in a cradle position, as if Timmy was still there, quietly asked, "Doctor, can you please help my baby." As the doctor quickly scanned the baby for any bones out of alignment he said confidently, "I will give it my best shot."

The doctor skillfully adjusted Timmy's misaligned neck creating an ever so slight pop. All of a sudden Timmy started to wail. Jane snapped out of her catatonic state and headed straight for the doctor thinking that he had done something bad to Timmy. Grace grabbed hold of Jane with all of her might and whipped her around to face her. As Grace shook her vigorously, she yelled, "When was the last time Timmy screamed and cried like this?"

With a quizzical expression, and realizing earlier he could hardly breathe, tears began to run down Jane's face as she simply said, "Never . . . never."

"Then let the doctor do his work and sit down!" Grace told Jane sternly.

A couple more adjustments and the doctor was done. Jane ran over to the adjusting table, picked little wailing Timmy up and hugged and kissed him. At that moment Jane knew that everything was going to be all right. Within a few minutes of the adjustment, Timmy had gotten enough oxygen to his body that his normal color had been re-established. Jane looked down into those big brown eyes of Timmy's and noticed that there was a more vibrant life force she had not seen previously. "See, Timmy, Mama told you everything would be all right," Jane softly assured Timmy as tears of joy streamed down her face.

The boy's name wasn't really Timmy. It was Richard— my name. This is my story. I am here today because of chiropractic. I am not sure why my family waited until 1999 to tell me this story, but nevertheless, I have decided to devote my life to that which saved my life.

Richard Betts
(Future D.C.)

"Can you recommend a good Chiropractor?"

Reprinted by permission of Peter Cranton.

Awakened

Sirens wailed out into the night breaking the silence of a sleepy suburban neighborhood. Ambulance, police units and fire engines raced to our home. My baby had stopped breathing and had begun to shake uncontrollably. Her face pale and body blue, I could do nothing as I looked into her sweet, baby-blue eyes fluttering back into her head. I had no knowledge of life support or how to make her breathe again. I had to pray and hope that the doctors could help her.

In the emergency room, I got little more than a pat on the back as I was, time and time again, sent home with this injured, weak, pile of lifelessness that so desperately frightened me.

As the months went by, the calls to 911 became more frequent until the calls were a daily event. Doctor after doctor diagnosed scarlet fever, rheumatic fever, flu, ear infection, neurological deficiency, and teething. In spite of the fact there was no substantial or coinciding symptomatology, we would be given a prescription for antibiotics and Tylenol. My questions were never answered. My fears were never confronted. *Would she die? Is she suffering damage during these increasing events?* And these seizures never stopped.

I quit my job, quit sleeping, quit eating and quit living, just as Blakely had already done. I'm not sure how, exactly, any of us remained alive at that time. I rested each day with Blakely atop of me so I could feel when—not if— she stopped breathing. I hoped that my filling her full of the drugs would keep her alive, but I knew in my heart that it would not—at least not for long. We all held our breath as she took each of hers.

My final day of tolerating this chaos came before Blakely's first birthday when she had suffered through ten to twenty seizures throughout the day. Something had brought enough courage to a friend for him to call me and tell me how chiropractic had "cured" his epilepsy, and I thought, *What could it harm?*

I called a co-worker who had been attending Logan College of Chiropractic and asked her for a reference for the best pediatric chiropractor in the area. I called and went in for an appointment that day. Dr. Burke took a detailed history of Blakely's short life and adjusted her. With no knowledge of chiropractic, I of course was skeptical. But more than that, I was desperate with hope. Dr. Burke did not poke Blakely or prod her, or hurt her in any way. As a matter of fact, Blakely seemed to enjoy the procedure.

I was sent home with information that my vegetative child would sleep for hours, wake and eat and play joyfully. That I doubted, as she had not done any of those activities in months. Well, guess what? She did all of the aforementioned, and a whole lot more. It was as if she had been awakened from a deep and restful sleep. I had my baby back. We, of course, had to develop a plan for her health care maintenance, but have had very few problems since. Blakely is a now healthy ten-year-old girl with the most beautiful smiling blue eyes you would ever want to see.

Christine Rockel

Nobody Likes a Colicky Baby!

Little Andrea came to my office at the age of two and a half months for the condition of colic at the urging of grandma, who is a patient of mine. Mom was also a patient who was helped with migraine headaches and lower back pain during her pregnancy with Andrea.

Andrea's mom had a long delivery, which can put stress on the baby's neck and middle back. From the beginning, Mom stated that life with Andrea was miserable due to her being colicky. During her maternity leave, it took hours to get ready to go grocery shopping—it was an all-day event. Often, they had to leave the grocery store early due to Andrea's constant crying. At night she was up every two hours crying, and it took one half hour to one hour to get her to go back to sleep.

On baptism day there were five babies being baptized, and Andrea cried throughout the entire ceremony. Grandma was often the babysitter and she called Andrea the "Screamer." "We've got to get this handled," Grandma said.

As the consultation continued, I explained to Andrea's mom that colic is a digestive disorder where gas is formed in the baby's stomach and small intestine. This causes much pressure and pain for the baby in these areas, which makes the baby irritable, with inconsolable crying and it arches its back a lot. Mom said Andrea was experiencing these same symptoms and she was told that this was a condition that her child would just have to eventually outgrow.

To ease her concern, I explained that the spinal adjustment for a baby is altogether different from a traditional manual manipulation adjustment for an adult. It is very light, gentle, and not at all uncomfortable for the baby.

Mom was excited and Andrea started care that day. Mom noticed improvement right away. Andrea could sleep better during the night. Now mom could take her shopping without the constant crying. She could also be taken to family gatherings without being disruptive. She was completely over her symptoms in thirty days, and then was put on a wellness plan.

Grandma said that after chiropractic care, Andrea was a lot of fun to play with because she was now quiet and content.

Now, Mom is a big supporter of bringing a baby to a chiropractor for colic. Two and half years later, Mom states that Andrea has not had the many ear infections and colds that other babies and toddlers often get. She says that bringing Andrea to me was the best thing she could have done for her.

It gave me tremendous satisfaction as a chiropractor to give Andrea a healthy start in life!

Kurt R. Schaarschmidt, D.C.

Jacob's Story

When Jacob was born he was a perfectly healthy baby. Lisa and I anticipated his arrival with the typical exuberance that accompanies a parent's firstborn. Life was smooth, fun and easy as Jacob developed into a healthy infant, and he brought us tons of joy. Then, the accident happened.

It was a Saturday morning in August 1990 when Jacob (at ten-months-old) accidentally slipped and fell backwards off of his bed. He landed on his head and rolled over, crying from fear and discomfort. Lisa grabbed him immediately and held her crying son, trying to alleviate his pain and distress. All seemed normal for the next few minutes as Jacob got back down on the floor crawling, until all of a sudden he stopped, laid down and closed his eyes. It's amazing how your life can turn in an instant.

Frantically, watching our child lay motionless on the floor, Lisa called me at the office in a panic about what had occurred. She described his semiconscious state, unstable breathing, and motionlessness. As a chiropractor, I immediately knew that his injury was serious, but I couldn't imagine what would follow.

When Lisa arrived at my office, I took one look at Jacob

and panicked myself. I informed my assistant to cancel the rest of my appointments for the morning; we had a serious problem on our hands. Jacob's paralysis was obvious. I immediately x-rayed his neck and there was no spinal fracture. The examination revealed a severe subluxation, or spinal imbalance causing pressure on his spinal cord and nerves. My hands were shaking so much from seeing Jacob in this state that I was unable to be objective.

I brought him to a chiropractic friend to see if he could help, but he also was overwhelmed by the lifelessness of Jacob, so we headed off to the local children's hospital. The staff at the hospital recognized the severity of Jacob's condition and rushed him back for extensive testing. Additional x-rays and CT scans were performed, and it was at midnight that we received the dreaded prognosis from the head of pediatric neurology.

Showing us the films, and with a grim tone in his voice, the medical expert told us the following, "Your child has had a severe stroke. Due to the extent of the damage, he will probably never walk, never talk and never use his right arm again." We were devastated.

The next two hours were a cycle of hysterical crying, disbelief, denial and a journey back to faith. A pediatric intensive care unit can be a very scary and lonely place at two o'clock in the morning, even with friends and family around.

Two hours later, with my brother Noel at my side, I was wheeling Jacob's bed around the pediatric intensive care unit when I heard the voices of my mentors telling me, "The power that made the body can heal the body. Take the pressure off the nerves and give the body the best chance to heal. Clear the interference in the mind-body connection and keep it clear for the rest of his life."

I turned to Noel and said, "I've got to get the pressure off the nerve."

At that moment, I lay my hands on Jacob's neck, found the subluxation, and adjusted him. The audible sound of the adjustment was so loud, which is very unusual in a baby, that it startled the nurses on duty and they immediately threatened to call the police on me because they weren't sure what I was doing.

I didn't care. It was obvious. The pressure was off the nerve and I could see and feel the life begin to flow back into Jacob's body. I ran out to Lisa who was resting in the waiting area and woke her up saying, "Lisa, I got it. I got the pressure off the nerve."

Within twenty minutes, Jacob woke up and his breathing stabilized. A few minutes later he was turning his head from side to side and showed signs of moving. His healing accelerated quickly, and within a few days he was crawling using just one side of his body. In less than two weeks he was pulling himself to a sitting position and crawling around the house.

By Jacob's first birthday, he was standing. At thirteen months he was walking, and at fourteen months, he was running with a limp. Our lives were filled with hope and possibility once again. While his right side continued to develop more slowly than his left, our constant stimulation, chiropractic adjustments, and belief in his ability to be whole and healthy kept us determined and motivated about his future. Unfortunately, the medical experts did not have the same faith. They told us that Jacob would probably not be able to ride a bicycle or roller blade, because the area of his brain that was injured had also affected his balance.

This was socially devastating to Jacob as he watched his younger siblings, Emily and Cory, perform these activities with ease. I remember trying to teach Jacob to ride a bike when he was eight years old, struggling to keep his balance and keep from falling. The emotional pain was too much to bear for the both of us at times, but we kept the faith and kept on believing.

Lisa, through her commitment and research, found the National Association for Child Development. Through their evaluations and therapy recommendations, along with Jacob's ongoing chiropractic care and his incredibly determined spirit, he began riding his bicycle, rollerblading and doing everything the experts had said he wouldn't be able to do.

Jacob has grown to be an incredible young man and is now thirteen years old. Just a few months ago, in an incredibly emotional and moving service, Jacob was bar mitzvahed and accepted his rite of passage into manhood. This little boy, who experts said would never walk, talk or use his right arm, marched proudly up to the pulpit, lifted the heavy scrolls with both arms, and spoke proudly in two languages to a crowd of over five hundred people.

In May 2003, Jacob ran for Student Body President of his school. He stood up and, for the first time in public, acknowledged his injury to his peers. He told them that what he learned from his experience would make him a good president. At the end of the speech, he contributed three copies of the first edition of *Chicken Soup for the Chiropractic Soul* to the school's library in honor of his campaign.

He won the election!

As Lisa and I think back on what could have been, we are grateful for what our family has become through Jacob's healing.

I often wonder what Jacob's life would be like if he had never been injured. However, because of what he has experienced and learned from this journey, I wouldn't trade anything for the young man he has become.

Jacob's healing inspired me to write the following poem

that was put into a poster with a beautiful photo of Jacob with his sister, Emily, on the beach.

A Chiropractic World

I live in a Chiropractic World

A world free from drugs and disease
A world free from pain and suffering
A world free from poverty and war
A world free from anger and hostility
A world free from chemical imbalance and ill mental health
A world free from vertebral subluxation

I live in a Chiropractic World

A world full of love and happiness
A world full of health and vitality
A world full of peace and harmony
A world full of children laughing and playing
A world full of prosperity and vision
A world full of life and energy

I live in a Chiropractic World

Eric Plasker, D.C.

Apnea

"Can you help apnea, Doc?" thats the question from this gentle, kind grandmother. Her inquiry was for her grandson, Isaac, who was only two but suffered not only sleep apnea, but also apnea that would attack him during waking hours. Apnea is a condition where the body stops breathing for no known reason.

Isaac's episodes were as frequent as eleven times per day. He would be playing on the floor and suddenly turn cyanotic (blue) from not breathing. Isaac's mother was a nurse and would quickly rescue-breathe the child each time he suffered an episode.

I learned that the family lived in San Diego, almost a hundred miles from my office. I instructed the grandmother to have the child taken to a chiropractor for an examination to determine if chiropractic could help. This conversation was on a Thursday. On Monday, the mother and child showed up on my doorstep telling me that the boy's grandmother assured them that I could help apnea.

I quickly backpedaled and explained that if biomechanical problems could be found, then indeed, chiropractic could help this condition.

When I met Isaac, or Zach as we called him, I was a little

surprised. He was a two-year-old in a four-year-old's body. I expected to see a malnutrition case or a sickly looking child. He was anything but sickly looking. When I entered the consultation room, Zach was hiding under the chair. His mother apologized for his behavior, but I quickly understood as the history began to unfold. Little Zach had been pushed, pinched, prodded and examined with almost every imaginable test. He had undergone upper and lower GI tests, CAT scans, MRI exams, and an EMG, in addition to three separate spinal blocks.

It was no wonder he was hiding under the chair, scared at the prospect of seeing another doctor who would do who-knows-what to him. My heart immediately went out to Zach and his mother, Susan. A trained nurse, Susan had a monitor that only went off when Zach didn't breathe for twenty or more seconds. She was constantly afraid that she would sleep too deeply and miss the sound of the monitor. Therefore, her sleep patterns were grossly disrupted.

It was a pleasure to examine Zach. While I held him stationary so I could get some upright x-rays, my associate took the x-rays. The views revealed significant abnormal function in the neck—I could tell by the x-rays that he had suffered a blow to the back of the head. The space between the skull and atlas on a two-year-old should be approximately 3 to 5 millimeters. Zach had a 0-millimeter space.

The vertebrobasilar artery enters the skulls at this point. The majority of the central and posterior brain is supplied blood through this artery, so any minor movement of the child's head would compress this artery, thus decreasing blood and oxygen supply to the brain. The result was apnea.

As I described the x-rays to Zach's mom, her eyes filled with tears. I assured her that it was okay because we could treat his condition. This is that biomechanical disruption we needed to find in order for chiropractic to be the answer. She then assured me that her tears were tears of joy. No doctor to this point had given any diagnosis or hope for relief. Zach and Susan now had hope.

Since they lived in San Diego, I referred them to another chiropractor but they insisted on driving to my office. I said Zach would need four adjustments a week. We arranged for Zach to get adjusted before I closed for lunch, then again as soon as I opened after lunch. We developed a very quick rapport with this family. Zach is a child with a full capacity to give and receive love. Zach always greeted me with a very long and tight hug around my neck.

Zach responded very favorably to his adjustments. His apnea episodes decreased very rapidly. He went from eleven episodes a day, to one a week within the first week. After sixteen weeks of adjustments, we x-rayed Zach because he had gone an entire month without an episode. The x-ray revealed a total restoration of the space between his atlas and head.

Zach is now twelve years old, six feet tall, and weighs 175 pounds.

Zach has been involved in Tae-Kwon-Do for the past two years. He is not only strong and handsome, he is in honors classes in school. Zach tested the highest in his school on the SAT 9 test. He is a very special boy with an appreciation for life and an ability to love and laugh and share with all around him.

John Holland, D.C.

Can I Have a Cookie?

Upon returning home from a long three days of studying in Florida for my chiropractic license exam, I anxiously walked through my front door expecting to be greeted by my wife and kids. Instead I was stunned to find my wife talking on the phone with my two-year-old son on her chest. His head and eyes where rolled back, he was white as chalk, and was soaking wet with a 105 degree fever.

I asked my wife for the phone. The doctor said that it sounded like my son was severely dehydrated and this was a medical emergency. He suggested that I bring my son to the hospital immediately. I thanked him profusely and told him that I was a chiropractor who had just walked through the door, that I would evaluate the situation, and if needed I would be there as soon as possible. I then took my son from my wife, put him on the floor, examined his back, and adjusted his neck. Within thirty seconds his eyes focused on me, his color returned, and his temperature dropped. That's when he said to me, "Hi Daddy, can I have a cookie?" I have never questioned the power of a chiropractic adjustment from that day forward.

Jens Valle, D.C.

5

CHIROPRACTIC AND KIDS

The obvious is that which is never seen until someone expresses it simply.

Kahlil Gibran

A Changed Demeanor

There is a power within—a fountain head of unlimited resources—and he who controls it controls circumstances instead of it controlling him.

B.J. Palmer, D.C.

Being an out-patient clinic intern in my last year at Parker College of Chiropractic, I must say I was full to the brim with chiropractic philosophy, but short on experience. I was about three quarters of the way to my completion of clinic. My new patient, I'll call him José, was a rather small thirteen-year-old Hispanic boy with dark eyes, black hair and a sunken demeanor. His gaze was always down and his spirit broken. In her broken English, his mother related to me José's history as I perused the medical documents she handed me. It seems that José was dropped while a baby and had suffered seizures since he was six years old. He had been given every pharmaceutical drug the medical doctors had at their disposal, but none of them had helped much. His seizures were occurring about three times per week, with no warning. José withdrew deeper and deeper into himself, to the point that he no longer associated with his siblings, parents, or the world around him. His pattern was to stay by himself at school, never making any friends. As soon as he got home, he went straight to his room and stayed there until morning and it was time to go to school again. His meals were eaten alone in his room. This was one sad little boy.

When directly questioned, José would give one word answers, never looking up. I told him that I was going to do an examination. His non-verbal response was expressive of his feelings, "So what, do whatever, it won't matter anyway."

My examination of José's spine revealed subluxations of the neck. After processing the paperwork through the clinic channels, I was cleared to adjust José. His look of surprise after his very first chiropractic adjustment reminded me of a child seeing his first new bicycle under the tree; eyes wide open and his mouth slowly curling up at the edges into a huge smile, half relief that it didn't hurt, and astonishment that he lived through it.

I explained to José and his mother that he needed to come in three times a week for a few weeks and then we would do another examination. They agreed and returned uneventfully for three more adjustments. By this time, José was used to the sound of the adjustment and seemed to look forward to them. On the afternoon of the second week's first appointment, José's mother was so excited she could hardly contain herself. José just sat there with a big grin on his face as his mother tearfully and joyfully told me about the events of the night before.

José was in his room as usual while she was preparing dinner. The other children and her husband were playing games and watching television. As was her routine, she prepared a plate and took it to José's room. Knocking on the door to let her son know that dinner was there, the door swung open and José told her he wanted to eat at the table tonight with the others. This, she said, had not happened in years. José took his place at the table, which had remained empty for years, with the astonished, but elated, family. During dinner José's two sisters asked permission to go to the mall after dinner. To everyone's surprise, José asked if he could go as well. It had been years since he had interacted with his family. Now he wanted to eat with them, play with them, and even venture out into the world alone. His mother was in tears, José was in tears, and I was in tears. The only thing that had changed in his treatment regime was chiropractic adjustments. Now, this once sullen, lonely boy has blossomed into the active, happy, joyful teenager that God intended him to be.

Barry Gardner, D.C.

Angel

We must look for the opportunity in every difficulty instead of being paralyzed at the thought of the difficulty on every opportunity.

Walter E. Cole

It was late afternoon and I was just beginning my evening shift at the country club. As a single mother and college student, I had taken this part-time job to help make ends meet. Suddenly, my manager called me into the office. With one look at his face, I knew a mother's worst fear had just come true. I slumped into a chair and felt the color drain from my face as he gently told me that my daughter was just in an accident on the playground. A teenager was playing "helicopter" with the younger children. My six-year-old daughter, Angel, was injured when his hands slipped from her wrists as he spun her around and around. When Angel hit the ground, her twisted little body was completely paralyzed from the neck down. Her pain was so intense she could only whimper and call my name.

Her sitter ran for the phone to call me. Knowing how

strongly I felt about the value of chiropractic care, she wanted to get instructions before calling an ambulance.

I called my chiropractor. His office was closed for the day but he agreed to see Angel right away. I tearfully told him it would take me forty-five minutes to get to his office from work and that my neighbors would be bringing her strapped on a board, in the back of a pick-up truck.

After calling the sitter and telling her what to do, I raced for my car and headed back to town. The rush-hour traffic was heavy and the drive seemed to take forever. Almost an hour after I received the frantic call from the sitter, I rushed through the empty waiting room and into the hallway that lead to the treatment rooms.

X-rays revealed that nothing was broken. That calmed my racing heart. I entered the treatment room behind Dr. Bill and Angel. You can imagine my surprise when I looked into the worried faces of some eight to ten neighbors. My sitter stepped forward and quickly filled me in.

After asking them to take Angel to the chiropractor rather than the hospital, one person ran for their truck; another went for a flat board. Together, they strapped her onto the board while someone secured her head. Everyone jumped into the truck for the ride to the office. None of them had ever been to a chiropractor. I'm sure they thought I had lost my mind, but they honored my wishes and did what they could to make the trip as comfortable and safe as possible for Angel.

After getting Angel settled on the table, I stepped back with my neighbors and watched Dr. Bill take over. He was kind and gentle as he slowly made little adjustments to her twisted spine. He used an Activator (a small instrument that impulses the bone back into place), so it was difficult for anyone to assess exactly what he was doing. Suddenly, Angel wiggled her toes and then her feet.

After a few more adjustments, she could wiggle her

fingers, hands and arms. Finally, with a tiny click of the instrument, Dr. Bill adjusted Angel's neck. We all held our breath when he pushed the button that slowly raised the table into an upright position. Angel very gingerly pushed herself back and stepped off the table. Her pain was gone. Her range of motion was normal. Tears fell, and no one spoke as Angel wrapped her arms around Dr. Bill's long legs and hugged her face into his thighs.

When I tried to pay him for the x-rays and treatment, Dr. Bill Salsman refused to take my money. Now I knew beyond a doubt that this man was an instrument of God.

Carol J. Phillips, D.C.

Turning on the Power

Wonders are many, and none is more wonderful than man.

Sophocles

I had recently moved to Colorado and was taking a break after ten years in practice to finish writing a chiropractic suspense novel. I envisioned six-months of focused solitude, during which I would write and rewrite until I had created chiropractic's best-selling answer to the ubiquitous medical thriller. My wife was in her third trimester of pregnancy and we were enjoying extra time together, excitedly planning our home birth, and the first few months of our baby's life.

My wife's sister lived in our town and had been suffering from disabling vertigo for nearly two years. She had exhausted her medical options, finding no relief from specialists from across the state. I agreed to take a look at her and found that a vertebra in the top of her neck was out of alignment. I adjusted the bone into place, and within three or four visits she was well. She was so thrilled that she described the "miraculous cure" in her Christmas newsletter. I soon had people calling my home and showing up on my doorstep asking for help. My sabbatical was changing fast. I wanted desperately to share the message of chiropractic with the public through my novel, and needed time to finish, but it is difficult to turn people away when they are standing at the door asking for the power of chiropractic healing.

Riley was one of those people who appeared shortly after my sister-in-law's newsletter. His mother brought him to my house and asked if I could help him. Although he was two years old, Riley had never spoken a word. His skin was pasty, his face swollen, and his eyes were dull and unfocused. He was very agitated, and shortly after his arrival, fell on my floor screaming and flailing his arms and legs. His mother told me this was a frequent occurrence. She also told me that Riley was scheduled for surgery to insert tubes into his ears and that he had been on antibiotics most of his life for upper respiratory infections. She was afraid for him and was sure he was at least partially deaf.

My writing was soon far from my mind and I felt overwhelming compassion as I looked at this distraught mother and her sick child. I knew that the medical doctors who had examined this boy dozens of times had overlooked the most basic requirement for true health—a properly aligned spine. I had heard stories like Riley's many times and was excited to "turn on the power" by removing the subluxations from his spine. I wanted to help this little boy break through and experience life the way it should be—full of wonder and wellness.

Riley was unwilling to let me touch or examine him at first. I am sure he was expecting me to brandish an otoscope and insert it into his painful ears for a look, but I was not interested in that. I knew his ears were infected. I only wanted to feel his spine to find out what was going on.

Children are amazing creatures. They have a very keen sense and intuitively know when they are touched by someone who can give them what they desperately need. Riley became attentive when my fingers found the subluxated vertebra at the top of his spine. The bone was likely knocked out of alignment at birth. With a gentle movement of my hand, I adjusted the bone into proper position for perhaps the first time in Riley's life. His eyes immediately locked onto mine, and although he had never uttered a word, he spoke volumes at that moment.

For me, this is the most exciting moment in chiropractic, when a child, no matter how young, looks into my eyes and thanks me for doing something that he innately knew he needed. I believe this is as close to mental telepathy as humans can get.

The adjustment was complete and it was time for Riley to go, but he didn't want to leave. Riley had found what he had been searching for and he fought his mother all the way to the car. Riley's ears and nose soon began draining mucous, and that evening he spoke his first words to his mother. By the third visit to the makeshift office in my living room, Riley no longer had tantrums and his eyes became focused and clear. During the next year his vocabulary caught up with, and exceeded, many children's his age. Riley has not had an antibiotic since his first adjustment and I still see him for regular wellness visits to make sure his spine stays free from subluxation. He smiles and dives onto the adjusting table when it is his turn. I see his little sister and the rest of his family, and the dozens of friends and their children, that his mother has referred.

Now, I get up very early in the morning to do my writing so I can still make it to the office every day to "turn on the power" for children and their parents.

John Adams, D.C.

Healing a Dampened Heart

You can not solve problems with the same level of thinking that existed when the problems were created.

Albert Einstein

When I was eight years old, my mom and I set a goal. If I could go thirty days without wetting the bed, I could buy a new bed. I strived to accomplish this goal. I would avoid drinking anything late at night and I went to the bathroom right before I went to sleep in hopes that these things would help. As I lay in bed, I would talk to myself, trying to convince my body that there would be no wetting the bed that night. However, more often than not, I would awaken damp and disheartened. I felt like a failure.

This problem had been an almost unbearable plague to me. None of my friends had this trouble and it was an unrecoverable embarrassment every time it happened while I was staying overnight outside of my home. I grew to fear sleeping anywhere else. I can even remember being mortified when I stayed with my grandparents and they offered me diapers or covered the mattress in plastic material. I would blink back tears at my inability to explain to my friends the reason that I didn't want to spend the night at their house. Then I would run to my mom trying to weep out my insecurity. I could tell that my mom was pained for me, but as we traveled from doctor to doctor, I felt more and more hopeless. I thought there was definitely something wrong with me personally if all of these doctors couldn't figure out what was wrong. So I just kept striving for that new bed. *One day,* I thought, *I would try hard enough and it would work.*

My stepfather moved in with us during that same year of my life, and I stared in dumfounded shock as my mom relayed the embarrassing account of my problem. She told me that he was going to help me. "He's a chiropractor," she said. *What the heck is a chiropractor,* I wondered. Then he pushed on my arm and cracked my back. He told me that he was making popcorn with my spine. I giggled as this new man told me to wiggle my toes while he adjusted my neck. I had no idea what he was doing, but at least he was funny. He had me take some nutrients, and he began adjusting me at night before I went to bed. I wasn't sure what any of this had to do with me wetting the bed. When I asked, he explained that everything was connected. Kinda like that old song, "The knee bone's connected to the ankle bone . . ."

This continued for awhile, and it wasn't long before I wasn't wetting the bed. One day, my mom approached me with a smile and asked if I was ready to go shopping for my new bed. I could barely believe it. I had hardly noticed, as not only one, but two months had gone by without my wetting the bed. My new bed was wonderful, and I began spending the night at friends' houses and feeling comfortable at overnight camp. Not long after that, my stepfather helped my brother to heal from his chronic asthma. Whatever this "chiropractic" thing was, I loved it.

Soon, this man had earned an invaluable place in my heart. One day I even asked him if I could call him daddy.

Amanda K. Gagnon

"Mommy, please read me the story where
Humpty Dumpty is referred to a Chiropractor
by Jack and Jill."

Reprinted by permission of Peter Cranton.

Now I Know That Grandma Loves Me . . .

Linda first came to our office because of chronic back problems that had started after a fall three and a half years earlier.

After seeing the chiropractor for about two weeks, her back problems went away. She was now able to do the things she had loved to do. She was an avid gardener, but pain had forced her to give it up. She was ecstatic because she could finally get back to her gardening. She was also a very proud grandmother, with the youngest grandchild being only two years old. Her grandchildren loved to spend the night at her house. This past weekend was different, though. She remembers her son coming to get the kids. Before leaving, Grandma reached down and picked up her youngest grandchild and gave her a big hug. The grandchild looked at her father and said, "Now I know that Grandma loves me."

The father looked at his daughter and said, "Of course, Grandma loves you. She always did."

The child said, "No, everybody who loves me picks me up and hugs me. Grandma never did, but now I know Grandma loves me."

Tears ran down Grandma's face. Back pain had

prevented her from picking up her grandchild, but chiropractic allowed her to demonstrate her love to her grandchild for the first time.

Pawel Pyrda, D.C.

The Big Picture

When the impossible has been eliminated, what-ever remains, no matter how improbable . . . is possible.

Sir Arthur Conan Doyle

Fifteen years ago, Allicia was only four and a half years old when I first saw her on the floor of my chiropractic office. I had just walked in to give Allicia's mother an adjustment, for her upper neck would "go out" and affect her vision; something surgery had not helped to correct. Allicia was blocking my way to the table to adjust her mother, so I asked Allicia to move, but she did not respond. Her mother turned her head up from the table headpiece and stated, "Allicia is deaf." I reached down to pick Allicia up and place her in the chair. I motioned for her to stay there. Allicia then mumbled and made contortionist-type facial expressions. Then her mother added, "Allicia is also retarded."

Oh! I thought, *a "special child" that my head instructor in school had taught me to respect and regard as a blessing to my office.*

While in student-clinic, I previously had great results with a two-year-old who was deaf and had an equilibrium problem. I began asking questions of Allicia's mother as soon as her adjustment was completed in hopes that I could check Allicia's spine. I learned that Allicia's deafness and brain damage was the result of multiple ear infections and high fevers. There was a second set of surgical drain tubes in her ears, with noted drainage coming out of the ear canals that day, which were still infected while on antibiotics. Allicia had remained on antibiotics almost continuously since she was eight months old. But something was allowing a continuous infection to remain.

I explained to Allicia's mother that I would like to evaluate her daughter and possibly treat her with chiropractic. The mother was hesitant, "We have spent thousands of dollars on her with drugs and surgery," was her comment. I asked her to look at her own condition that surgery did not correct. The vision problem continued following surgery, and when her neck was in alignment the vision improved. Further hesitation persisted due to the family buying a business in the commercial center where my office was also located. They were financially stressed, as are most new business owners.

Making it up on the spot, I said, "Children are treated complimentary when parents are treated as a tribute to family health." Whether I was too persistent, or the mother thought I was noble, it did not matter now. I was allowed to place Allicia on the adjusting table.

My hands told me Allicia's upper spinal vertebrae were rotated and restricted in what should be proper movement. I adjusted the vertebrae that needed it. The mother asked more questions as we walked to the door. Allicia took off towards her parent's business. I watched as she ran awkwardly down the sidewalk. The mother said, "That's strange. I have never seen her go more than a few feet without falling down when she runs."

Allicia finished the thirty-yard jaunt to the business with no falls. The mother waited a while, but brought her daughter back when the infection and drainage out of the ear dried up; curious as to whether the adjustment had an effect, or had the drugs just started to work.

After completing a series of adjustments over the next three months, Allicia was released from the school for the deaf, as her hearing was tested and was shown to be improving. In fact, it was now almost normal. The six therapists questioned the mother as to what therapy Allicia had performed over the summer to improve her conditions that much. Confusion was especially noted when chiropractic was the only thing mentioned. This was the last time she was on antibiotics for anything related to her ears, or other conditions, as far as I know.

Allicia was then ready for special education schooling where she has flourished. Her senior year, Allicia was inducted into the National Honor Society for Special Education. Allicia has competed in Special Olympics and has won multiple gold medals, as well as helped others. This month, I am invited to Allicia's graduation, along with the others who have helped her.

Allicia has grown up quite well and still deals with areas of her brain that were affected by the infections and high fevers. When Allicia was young and could not speak, she would grab her head and act like she was twisting the spine to render an adjustment in orders to communicate she wanted, or needed, an adjustment. The words for adjustment went from mumbles, to "justment," to "adjustment." She saw the big picture and communicated it the best she could throughout the years.

Allicia's mother tells me there have been people who doubt that chiropractic could have done anything to help her, let alone helped the restoration of the hearing and the healing of her repeated ear infections. She also tells me a little story she has used to make a point. Allicia accompanied her younger sister to a medical doctor's office for a physical. A physician's assistant performing the task asked if they saw any other doctors. Allicia replied, "Dr. Walford."

The P.A. did not know who I was and Allicia enthusiastically blurted out, "He is the one who cured my deafness." The P.A. looked at the mother and asked, "This is not a medical doctor, is it?"

The mother replied, "No."

As the P.A. went about the physical, he gathered more information about Allicia's improvement and finally asked, "Do you think the chiropractor healed your deafness?" Allicia, without missing a beat, answered, "Well, I can hear you can't I?"

Richard D. Walford, D.C., C.C.S.P.

Confidence to Conquer the World

In order to be a realist you must believe in miracles.

David Ben-Gurion

"Mommy, I just hate my life!" This cry of anguish and frustration was uttered from the lips of five-year-old Zachary. On the outside, Zach appeared to be a happy and active, loveable little boy. He was well liked by everyone who knew him. Inside hid an intelligent, yet confused, little boy. Zach was diagnosed with dyspraxia, a motor processing and sequencing problem where the information would get to his brain, but he could not take this information, organize it, and then perform the task at hand. It affected every facet of his life. The simplest things like getting dressed for school were stressful. Every morning his mom, Susan, would have to help him to get ready for school by giving step-by-step instructions for even the smallest task. Otherwise, what would normally take half an hour could take up to an hour and a half without his mom's loving prompting. Although Zach knew what to do, he could not organize his thoughts to do the smallest task. "Put your socks on. Now put your shoes on and brush your teeth." Occasionally, Zach's inner frustration would explode forth, "I can do it myself," he would yell at his mom. So every day started off in stress and unhappiness for everyone.

School was by no means a picnic. Every morning after fighting his mom to get ready, Zach went into a world where most students could process all types of information quickly and accurately. Zach was struggling to stay focused on school rather than play. At the age of five, he was below his grade level, he was clumsy and uncoordinated, and experiencing horrifying night terrors and nauseating migraine headaches. Migraine headaches, an adult malady, had gained entrance in the most precious years of life—childhood.

His condition also affected his social life. Riding a bike or hitting the ball with his friends, things that we all take for granted, took tremendous concentration for Zach. By the time the ball had reached Zach, he was still processing the fact that it had left the pitcher's hand. And by the time he realized, it had passed him. This made organized sports a struggle. But Zach had great friends who accepted him for the wonderful person he was and not for how well he played baseball or rode a bike.

Vowing to find help for her son, Susan consulted with Zach's teachers for help. She was told he was young. "He needs to mature; give it some time."

By the age of seven, he had seen specialists—from behavioral and occupational therapists, to ophthalmologists and neurologists—to no avail. A true blessing to Zach and his family was Zach's third grade teacher, who not only knew of his problem, but understood it. It was as if an angel had appeared. She offered to tutor Zach on processing skills and building his short- and long-term memory.

Taking advantage of this first positive step, Susan decided to investigate what would be referred to as "alternative" medicines instead of traditional medicine. She first consulted her aunt, a nutritional consultant. She recommended a healthier diet and vitamin supplements. This helped, but Susan could not help but feel that there was still something missing. Her aunt then recommended seeing an atlas orthogonal chiropractor to make sure there was not a misalignment. After taking x-rays, it was found that Zach had a severe imbalance in his first vertebrae. This was interfering with oxygen flowing freely to the brain and consequently blocking and slowing informational pathways. Although it made sense and Susan was hopeful, she hesitated.

After a brief exam and a review of his records, I adjusted Zach's atlas and prayed that I would be able to help him. *No child or family should have to suffer like he has,* I thought to myself. After the first correction, Zach said he felt better and unconsciously let out a sigh of relief. After hearing Zach's words and sigh of relief, Susan knew she had done the right thing and was looking forward to a new beginning. It was a couple of weeks later after his first adjustment Zach ran into the office: HE WAS ABLE TO RIDE A TWO-WHEEL BICYCLE. Everyone in the office cheered and celebrated with Zach and his mom. His joy was palpable. Here was a little boy finally beginning to enjoy life. Zach was on a roll and there was no stopping him now that he had gotten started.

About a month later, Zach came running into the office, again grinning from ear to ear. He handed Dr. Leslie a test paper and on it was the biggest, brightest letter "A" you ever saw. He told Dr. Leslie that this was the first "A" he had ever got in school. When I looked at Zach, I could actually *feel* his joy and sense of accomplishment. Here he was, an intelligent little boy, now, for the first time in his life, he had the grade to prove it!

Zach also began to prove his prowess on the baseball field. He had become such an important part of the team, that inevitably, a day or two before a game (sometimes even every day), Zach would come in for an adjustment because the team depended on him.

The phrase, "Mommy, I just hate my life," once uttered in total frustration, had now been replaced with, "Mommy, I'm proud of me."

Throughout his ordeal of dyspraxia, Zach learned an invaluable lesson about himself and his body. Misplacing things is not a sign of being lazy and disorganized; instead he is disorganized and cannot focus because he is in need of an adjustment. Now, at the age of eleven, Zach is the first one ready for school in the morning and actually looks forward to learning new things every day. He is still playing organized baseball and has recently started basketball. The frustrated, clumsy child of five had faced off with his problem and won through chiropractic care. Now Zach is a happy and confident, pre-teenager ready to conquer the world.

Leslie M. Windman, D.C.
with Jeannine Marie L'Heureux

Chicken Soup Is Great . . . But Chiropractic Is Better!

Hope . . . is the companion of power, and the mother of success; for whose hopes strongly has within him the gift of miracles.

Samuel Smiles

Among my earliest memories, those remembered vividly as an adult, but actually lived as a child, was the undeniable fact that I was different than the other children on my block. They were healthy! They ran and played and had fun, never giving a second thought to the miracle they had in their possessions—abundant health. Nor, I guess, should they. After all, isn't it natural to be born healthy? Isn't that the way it is supposed to be?

Perhaps so, but that wasn't my experience. Instead, my world was filled with intermittent attacks of bronchial asthma that precluded my participation in normal childhood activities. I was relegated to a seat in the window of our five-story walk-up apartment in Brooklyn, New York, where, with a broken heart, I gazed down upon the other seven-year-old boys playing their games, oblivious to my suffering.

How I longed to play with them, but over-stimulation of any kind seemed to trigger an attack. And, like all children, I learned quickly. I remembered the time that such an attack landed me in a local hospital where I was placed in the restricted confines of an oxygen tent. To this day, I can see the face of the nurse as she opened up a corner of the tent, put in a fork full of peas for me to snap at, and then quickly closed the tent so as to keep the oxygen from escaping.

This wasn't great for my self esteem! And that wasn't the worst of it. I also suffered from Eczema, a skin condition that created a nasty looking, constantly itchy and very painful rash that covered my hands more particularly, my fingers. I could tolerate the pain, but I was embarrassed beyond belief at having to wear white gloves to cover the less than appetizing appearance of my fingers. It was not a pretty sight.

So what do parents do in such a situation? Mine, like all loving moms and dads, turned over every leaf looking for the remedy that would cure their ailing son. Doctor after doctor prescribed pills, potions, lotions and topical salves. I was taken to every imaginable doctor and any guru specialist who might be able to help. Finally, when all avenues were exhausted—with zero results I might add—my aunt told my parents of a different kind of a doctor, one who didn't rely on the use of drugs or medication, but rather looked to the nervous system and spine to find the cause of a person's disease.

Remember that this was 1947, and chiropractic was not yet even recognized as a licensed profession by the State of New York. My parents not only had no prior knowledge or belief system about chiropractic, but they, like so many before them, were instantly prejudiced because all they knew was traditional medicine.

Luckily, or should I say fortuitously, my aunt pounded away, telling stories of all of the amazing results that her doctor of chiropractic was achieving. Conditions such as neck and back, disc and sciatic problems, she said, were commonplace. While under care herself for numbness in her arms, she met patients who sought chiropractic for a large variety of ailments. They came in for headaches, digestive disturbances, colitis, irregular menstrual cycles and for relief from asthma and allergies, just to name a few. Finally, my parents relented since, according to my dad, they had nothing to lose and this was proverbially the last resort.

His office was just a few blocks from Ebbetts Field, then the home of the famed Brooklyn Dodgers baseball team. In fact, it was the year that Jackie Robinson broke the color line of our national pastime. Trust me when I report that this was not exactly the typical professional office I had become accustomed to visiting. No shingle outside, all patients by referral, one huge waiting room with no receptionist, and instead of just a few chairs circling the periphery of the room, there were about fifty chairs set theater-style. They all faced one door that led to a much smaller combination consultation, examination, and chiropractic adjusting room.

When we entered the office, no chiropractic assistant bounded out in a friendly and professional manner to greet us, or even give us that infamous clipboard to fill out and return to the front desk when we were finished. There was no front desk, just a room filled to capacity with people waiting to see the chiropractor.

We took a seat in the rear of this movie theater set-up and every few minutes someone would lean through the door I just described and a booming deep baritone voice would yell out, "Neeeext." Then, as if staged by a director, everyone in that reception room would stand up and move down to the next seat closer to the front as two people in the first two chairs got up and went in for their adjustment. And so it went, until we occupied chairs one, two, and three.

When our turn came and I heard that booming voice yell "next," I froze with fear and, literally, needed to be dragged in for what felt to me to be my execution. Anyhow, this 6'4" Doctor of Chiropractic, Benjamin Hershon, greeted us in a very friendly manner and then, without the traditional consultation taken by all those M.D.s I had visited, he delivered a short and powerful speech that would change my life forever. Paraphrasing, he said in his best inaugural address tone, that The human body is an amazing machine that has within it the innate intelligence and inborn potential to heal itself from within. When you are healthy, as you were meant to be, you don't give it a lot of thought, but chiropractors do. We feel that if the intelligence of the body can create you, and if it can regulate all of the thousands of body functions simultaneously in health, then when you are sick, it doesn't make sense for us to look outside of the body for the CAUSE of your DIS-EASE. We instead, wonder how the body can heal itself in health and fail to be able to do so when the body is ill. We ask what went wrong inside the body that is stopping it from healing itself. Good question, huh?

Dr. Hershon then, in a very quick and efficient manner, went on to tell us that there is a great possibility that some of the small bones in my spine were probably out of their normal alignment and were interfering with the normal flow of nerve impulses originating in the brain. Especially the ones that were supposed to tell my lungs what to do and how to react and adapt to their environment. Guess he heard me wheezing!

He also couldn't miss observing a seven-year-old

wearing white gloves. So, without missing a beat, he continued his spiel by telling my parents that my hands and fingers had nerve supplies too, and if they were interfered with, the rash could be the end result. His certainty was compelling, and when he said that, if indeed this was the problem, chiropractic could probably help. Well, it was music to our ears; euphoria to our hearts!

What followed was an examination and x-ray study to determine the presence of those subluxations, and a program of care to locate and remove them so the nervous system could function unimpeded and the intelligence within the body could do its thing again and heal itself naturally!

And, so we went. Three times per week for a long time, then twice a week. Then, with time, once per week, and finally, every other week for a few years. He told us this was not about symptoms, and when they went away we were not to go away until the cause, the vertebral subluxations, were also gone.

A year or so later, the results were amazing. No more wheezing, no more white gloves. Healthy lungs and hands that I keep manicured because I am proud to show them off.

I spent the rest of my childhood running and playing and carrying on like any NORMAL child, but there was a difference. I decided that when I grew up I wanted to become a chiropractor and to help other people lead healthy and happy lives too.

Chicken Soup is Great . . . But Chiropractic is Better.

Larry Markson, D.C.

The Things We Don't Do

Everything should be as simple as it is, but not simpler.

Albert Einstein

It was during my first year in my new practice, when one of my established patients, Vicki, presented for care. She had with her on that day her young son. When I finished with her treatment, I inquired about her son. Vicki was reluctant to take up my time as I had other patients waiting, but she seemed relieved that I had asked.

It seems that he had been running a mild fever and "just seemed out of it." Acquiring her permission, I performed a cursory examination, feeling his neck for the presence of lymph nodes, and checking his temperature. He was indeed running a low-grade fever of 99 degrees. I was uncomfortable with the absence of lymph nodal involvement with the presence of a fever and asked her if she had noticed any other symptoms or changes in his behavior. She reported that he hadn't gone to the bathroom even though he was usually quite regular.

I took this new information and performed light

palpation over the abdomen, finding mild tenderness over the right lower quadrant, and described it so a patient would understand. They were classic signs for an appendix-related problem. I informed her that she should go to see her family doctor. Vicki told me that she had been there earlier that day and he had informed her that it was a virus. I suggested that she should then go to the emergency room to have him evaluated. Vicki was reluctant, as she had just seen the doctor. I relayed my concerns about his lack of elimination, the fever, and the fact that this is something chiropractors don't do. She agreed to have him checked.

I had heard nothing further from them. She was pain-free and didn't return. However, on a Saturday during the local Business Expo, a woman I didn't know approached me and told me that I had saved her grandson's life. Sensing my confusion she smiled, patted my shoulder, and walked slowly away. I was at a loss. Then Vicki came up to me and with tears in her eyes, said to me; "You saved my son's life." I saw the stranger over Vicki's shoulder smiling at me.

Vicki asked me if I had remembered that day in my office. She told me how, even though she thought it senseless, she had taken her son to the emergency room and, equipped with the information I had given her, told the physicians to check her son. Vicki, through the tears in her eyes, went on to say that they did emergency surgery on her son, removing his inflamed appendix. When the procedure was finished and her son was out of danger, the surgeon told her that the appendix was about to rupture and that if she had waited two hours longer, the prognosis wouldn't have been good.

Overwhelmed and through tears of my own, I told Vicki that I really didn't DO anything. She disagreed with me, and with steel in her eyes, said that had I not listened to her on that day, she may have just gone home and put her son in bed to rest and he may never have awakened. Vicki smiled at me, and then, as she could see her words sink in, gave me a hug and walked away.

I stood, as if in shock, and thought about her words. A warm sensation traveled over my entire body as I thought about the little boy who now walked hand-in-hand with his mom, and about the things we as chiropractors don't do.

Dr. Steven W. Blevins, D.C.

I Love Being a Chiropractor

The magic bullet of all healing is love.

Dr. James W. Parker

He looked up at me with brown eyes that said more than his own voice could. He was suffering. He was not a happy child like his brother was. He rarely smiled. He rarely spoke. When he did, it was an effort, and a raspy whisper was all he could muster. Patrick, a redheaded three-year-old, was born with Recurrent Laryngeal Papilloma (RLP), which means he had warts on his vocal cords, which keep growing. Warts are a virus, and as we know, there is no medical treatment for viruses. So since birth, Patrick has undergone laser surgery to burn off the warts every four weeks! This included sticking a scope through the nose and down the throat to survey the number and location of warts. Then, he was anesthetized and laser surgery was performed; every four weeks for three years of his life. That is more than thirty operations by the time I met him. The laser surgery was simply a band-aid, removing the warts until they would return and grow large enough to have to laser off. With each surgery, more scar tissue would grow on his vocal cords. Not only was each surgery an inconvenience and a risk, each surgery was also slowly scarring Patrick's voice, until one day, he would lose it. He had an oxygen machine at home to test his oxygen level daily. If it went below 90 percent, that meant the warts were returning, blocking his airway. New drugs, such as Interferon, a cancer drug, are being used with some success, but most people with RLP do not live a full lifespan.

I heard about Patrick through a friend, so I arranged to meet with his parents to talk about the possibilities of chiropractic with Patrick's case. I showed them that chiropractic adjustments could help boost the immune system; a proven fact. Patrick's parents were young and without money. With that, I began adjusting Patrick at no cost, with the intent that a better immune system can fight off viruses. I had no guarantees for his parents. Who knew what the body would do? But he was young, and I had a driving faith that chiropractic can let the body do powerful things.

I set out with my adjusting instrument in my hand, chiropractic knowledge in my head, and God's power in my heart.

After a few months of regular adjustments, Patrick's doctors told him he did not have to return for six weeks, then eight weeks, then twelve. Patrick's color returned to his cheeks, he was speaking more often and with more sound. His colds and coughs were even less frequent. He was happy and playful and he loved seeing me walk into the room. He may not have known why or how, but he knew he felt better after I worked on him. So while I was working on him, the MD's continued to put the scope down his throat every few months to see that surgery was not necessary, yet again; that no warts had grown since his last visit. Soon his medical doctor would just shake his head and say, "See you in three months."

After an unheard of fifteen months without surgery in this young boy's five long years of life, Patrick's mom came into my office after his latest appointment and looked at me with tears in her eyes. She said, "They don't want to see him for six months." I ran over to Patrick, picked him up and hugged him hard.

Christine Maguire, D.C.

A Neighbor's Encounter

There is no medicine like hope, no incentive so great, and no tonic so powerful as expectation of something tomorrow.

Orison Swett Marden

As I reached into the cold, metal box to retrieve my mail, I heard a warm, familiar voice say, "Hello, neighbor." It was Charlie, my next door neighbor. I welcomed Charlie home from his recent travels and inquired about his well being. He was doing great, he said, but I detected a hint of worry in his enthusiasm. I expressed my concern to Charlie and he shared with me the story of his eleven-year-old granddaughter, Torie.

The words Charlie spoke were that of a little girl suffering. A little girl, who, for the past seven weeks, could not stop vomiting. A little girl who had been examined by the top GI specialists at Texas Children's Hospital. All this only to hear, "We cannot find anything wrong with you." Three separate prescription medications were administered and she was told, "If you lose three more pounds, you will need a feeding tube."

I explained to him how vital the nervous system is to health. I continued, describing how interference on the nerves distorts the message from the brain and that this can lead to disease. If Torie had interference on the nerves controlling her digestive tract, then this could be the cause of her illness.

I felt passion and hope and worry; all at the same time. I was passionate with the chiropractic truth, hopeful that Charlie would pass this information to his family, and worried that he would not.

I was elated and relieved when Torie's mother, Katherin, phoned. Her voice was heavy with concern for her daughter, and laced with skepticism about chiropractic. With her last bit of hope she uttered, "We don't know what else to do, but how is chiropractic going to help my daughter stop vomiting?"

I explained to Katherin how, through chiropractic, the nervous system should be free of interference for true health to be present and that I would like for her to consider bringing her in. I met Torie the very next morning.

Torie shuffled into the clinic early the next day. She was thin, fragile, weak, tired, and pale, with exception to the dark circles under her eyes. In her hands she carried a pink rubber bucket to collect her vomit. She vomited so often that she was afraid to be without it. She was nervous and unsure of what she might be subjected to next.

As I talked with Torie and her family, I came to understand the full impact Torie's illness had on them. Torie could not attend school with her friends. She had a teacher coming to the house. She could no longer play on her softball team, go to orchestra practice, or attend Girl Scout meetings. Katherin was close to losing her job because of all the time off she had taken to be with Torie. Family time as a whole had been consumed with worry over Torie.

After careful evaluation of Torie's condition, I felt confident to report my findings. I knew in my heart that chiropractic could help Torie. I had heard of such grand miracles in chiropractic. So why not this? Sitting in the dimly lit report room, I told Torie and her family that I could make no guarantees. Torie received her first and second adjustment that day.

We continued adjusting twice a day for nine days. Torie's diet also had to be assessed.

By the third day, Torie had gone from vomiting throughout the day, to only vomiting a few times a day. By the end of the first week she was only vomiting once or twice a day. Torie was unrelenting with her progress. She went from actually vomiting to merely a reflux type of spitting up. Torie was enjoying many consecutive days symptom-free within four weeks.

That is when I got to meet the real Torie, a girl with puffy cheeks, a funny little laugh, sparkly eyes with no dark circles beneath them, and all the sass that goes with being eleven. Her social calendar is filled with family outings, church picnics, and Girl Scout camp-outs.

Torie has now spent several months free of symptoms. Torie's mother, Katherin, says chiropractic is a God-send. God sent Charlie and me to the mailbox that Saturday afternoon so that we could bring chiropractic into Torie's life.

April Nelson, D.C.

"Dr. Kevin, will you adjust Molly,
she had a rough holiday season."

Reprinted by permission of Peter Cranton.

A Father's Story

The art of medicine consists in amusing the patient while nature cures the disease.

Voltaire

My son Tim's first visit to a chiropractor, Dr. Ciro Rustici, was born of desperation. Cerebral palsy had confined this handsome, brilliant child to a wheelchair-based existence since birth, but the shenanigans of our insurance company had delayed the financing and construction of a new, appropriately sized wheelchair for nearly a year. During that time, the onset of adolescence had added nearly seven inches to his slender frame and he was poorly postured and unsupported in the child-sized wheelchair in which he had lived during his waking hours for the past five years.

Tim was in constant pain with severe back and lower abdominal cramping, and hadn't slept for more than ten minutes at a time for nearly six weeks. A week and a half prior to his first chiropractic visit, a full regimen of body scans and internal probes at a world-class children's hospital had resulted in no diagnosis. The codeine he had been prescribed did little to alleviate his discomfort, but did have the unfortunate side effect of inhibiting bowel movements—he hadn't pooped once in ten days!

By the time we arrived at Ciro's, Tim's existence had been reduced to curling into a fetal position, whether in his wheelchair, or in bed at night. Any attempt to straighten his legs or torso resulted in unbearable pain. His voice, airy and thin before, had been reduced to a whisper. His complexion was sallow, his eyes rolled back in his head and he drooled incessantly.

Instead of transporting Tim in his chair, I opted to cradle his seventy pounds in my arms and carry him from the truck into the office. Although I received the same warm greeting from the receptionist that I'd come to expect, there was also a definitive expression of utter pity as she gazed upon Tim for the first time. I had described Tim's situation on the telephone, but the harsh reality of his condition was more than she had expected.

We were quickly ushered into the examination and treatment area—a large room with a half dozen treatment tables, three drop tables, and three chiropractors who attended a steady stream of patients. Dr. Rustici immediately came to our side and helped me lower Tim onto the table. He issued a sharp yelp as we tried to lay him face down—he was just incapable of lying flat. It was too darn painful. Together we sat him up and Ciro palpated his hunched neck and torso. "His atlas is acutely subluxated," pronounced Ciro. "Let's put him on the drop table."

This part was actually quite simple. Tim's fetal posture was a perfect fit for the treatment and in his exhausted state he offered little resistance. Dr. Rustici gently explained the procedure to Tim and adjusted the table. I noticed that a hush had come over the room. The two other doctors and a room full of patients were transfixed on this scene. Even the receptionist, business manager, and patients from the waiting area peered in through the doorway. Ciro carefully placed the edge of his right hand at an angle on the side of Tim's neck and, bracing it with his left, pushed forward and down. The table's headpiece dropped with a resounding thud.

A moment passed and then in a voice as clear as Church bells on a cold winter's eve, Tim exclaimed, "that felt great." As though a switch had been thrown, the color flooded back into his face, and he straightened his body. A short time later, with Ciro's assistance, he sat up on the edge of the table. "Are you ready for me to carry you to the truck?" I asked. Unbelievably, he responded, "I think I'll try to walk Dad—will you help me?" Hooking my fingers under his armpits, he slid off the table, came to a standing position, and then with my support, like a newly oiled Wizard of Oz Tinman, took a step. And then another. And another, and another.

When we had covered the twenty-five feet between the examination room and the front door, Tim wasn't yet ready to leave. He insisted on shaking hands and conversing with everyone in the outer waiting area. Looking around me, I noted a lot of eyes being rubbed with sleeves and dabbed with Kleenex. As we finally headed towards the exit, Tim asked to linger for a moment at the front desk where he had spied a large container of Sponge Bob Square Pants stickers—his favorite.

As he made his choices, that same receptionist who'd greeted us thirty minutes earlier leaned over and whispered, "I've witnessed a lot of amazing recoveries over the years, but never anything like that." And each week since, with his stepmother, brother and sisters joining us for regular adjustments, that amazing recovery continues.

Terry Bartow

Asthma

If at first you don't succeed, try, try, try again.

William E. Hickman

Shortly after my son turned eighteen months old, I rushed him to the hospital for the first time. As he struggled in my arms to take each breath, the doctors said Christopher was having an asthma attack. Time and time again over the years, I would find myself back in the emergency room, holding my son and begging for answers for this condition that seemed to be robbing my son of his childhood.

With the daily doses of Theophyline that followed, various inhalers and weekly blood checks, he only seemed to be getting worse as he grew up. Each attack became more severe, and no one was able to explain to me *why* this was happening or how we could prevent it.

By the time Chris was four years old, he was undergoing immunotherapy with weekly allergy shots, blood work and increased medications. The trips to the emergency room continued, and I wasn't sure if he even knew what breathing well felt like. He walked and played with his shoulders elevated and he worried constantly whether something was going to happen. We did everything we were told, short of raising him in a bubble, but still, the attacks came.

After moving to a new house out of the city and renting a pulmo-aid/breathing machine as the doctor had instructed, things seemed to be improving. For the first time, we began to think that Chris might be outgrowing his asthma, as the doctors told us he might. Within a year, however, Chris was sick again, with every common cold and change of season landing him right back in the E.R.

When Chris was seven, he contracted scarlet fever. I rushed him to the closest hospital and was told this time that he would not be coming home with me. We were told that the scarlet fever had brought on a severe asthma attack that had collapsed the lower lobe of his right lung. Chris was hospitalized for over a week and his discharge brought with it a radical change in his medications, more breathing treatments, and subsequent visits to lung specialists—the bills added up!

Within a month, Chris was sick again and his new pediatrician suggested that Chris start swimming in order to exercise and strengthen his lungs. Chris joined a community swim team and it seemed to be the answer to our prayers. We thought that it might be a way to get Chris better without just giving him more medications. Chris was having a lot of fun swimming in competition and he was pretty good at it! Unfortunately, the breathing problems he encountered whenever he had to swim distances over fifty meters was proof that his asthma was still a reality.

Chris was almost ten and swimming at the top of his age group on our community's United States Swim Team when his right lung collapsed for the second time. This time, however, he was hospitalized in intensive care. They said his right lung was down and in his "good lung," on the left, he had pneumonia. After this nearly two week long hospital stay, the doctors said that we needed to get more medically "aggressive" with Chris' type of asthma if we wanted to prevent his from happening again. So . . .

All of Chris' medications were increased, and steroids were added, and three weeks to the day after his hospital discharge, on Halloween night in 1992, we almost lost Christopher to yet another attack. Now I was unable to even be at his side, as the doctors worked around him in the critical care unit. His right lung was collapsed and his left lung was hyper-extended. All I could do was pray to God that He would save my son. I didn't want to lose him!

God answered my prayers, and late in the following day, Christopher's condition was upgraded and he moved to intensive care. Within a few weeks, he was back home and I was back to the grind of following all the discharge instructions; taking Chris back to begin immunotherapy *again* (this time he would be put through the 110 shot/scratch test), and trying to deal with his daily emotional swings that were inevitably a side effect to all the medications. Like a "good mother," I drove him weekly to get his shots, kept his medications stocked at home, had him check his breathing patterns on his peak flow meter (every chance I got), kept him away from his friends and family members who had pets, made him play inside during dreary weather, and put my foot down on the "dangerous activities" such as roller skating parties (where public smoking might occur), camping (where there might be a bon fire) and trips to the zoo (obviously). We all did our part or what we thought we had to do to keep Chris healthy. Despite all our efforts, Chris would get sick again! Before he turned eleven, he went into intensive care once more with a collapsed right lung and a hyper-extended left lung. Only this time he needed to be isolated, "due to a virus," they told us, and I wondered, *quarantine for asthma?* The doctors told us that Christopher had R.S.V., a virus common to preemies and newborns with weak lungs or poor immune systems. I couldn't believe it! My son had been born perfectly healthy and now, ten years later, his lungs were as susceptible to infection as a premature baby's would be. *Chris wasn't going to "outgrow" his asthma, his asthma was going to outgrow him,* I thought.

Well, when Christopher finally left the hospital, this time we visited a chiropractor. Dr. Dionne had been telling me all along about the benefits of chiropractic for total- body health, but I never thought that this was an option for Christopher with all his serious attacks and his need for such intense medical interventions. Although I was skeptical, I was willing to try anything that might help Chris with his asthma, where nearly a decade of everything else had seemed to fail. I was so afraid that I could lose my son if we continued to care for him as we had, that I reached "that point" where even the most "unconventional" approach looked good to me. I just didn't want to lose him; I didn't want to see my son suffer—not for one more day.

I can't explain why or how, but for Christopher, chiropractic adjustments worked! I started to believe a little in our "new approach" when I noticed he was less dependant on his inhalers and was using his breathing machine fewer and fewer times. I couldn't become a true believer, however, because autumn was about to come. But when autumn turned to winter, and for the first time Chris hadn't missed a day of school due to asthma, I began to *REALLY* believe that something was finally right; that we were doing the right thing for our son by having him under chiropractic care.

When winter turned to the ever-dreaded spring, I knew it was truly time to put chiropractic to the test. Chris continued to get adjustments once a week and stayed healthy until the flu bug entered our house. All three of our other children caught the flu, and then, so did Chris, and I knew what was about to happen. In a week and a half the flu had run its course, and yet, I was still waiting to have to run Chris into the E.R. for breathing problems. But nothing more serious than the flu hit Chris, and before we knew it, spring was turning to summer.

By the end of the summer, Chris was swimming at his best in U.S. Swimming competitions. He was medaling at state finals, and he qualified for the highest level of competition for U.S. age group swimming, sending him all the way to Nebraska for the U.S. Central Zone Championships. After swimming well and staying healthy in the 112-degree heat of Lincoln, Chris came home with the thought that chiropractic had finally cured him. He felt so good that he stopped going in for adjustments.

It had been almost a year since Chris' last visit to a medical doctor, but when he had stopped going in for adjustments, he noticed that within a month or two he needed to use his inhalers more frequently. We wondered if this was just due to another season change, but when we went in to his pediatrician for his school physical (so that he could participate on school sports teams), he was prescribed a new medication that was supposed to help him with his "night" asthma. I reluctantly put Chris on this new form of Theophyline and in three weeks, he was back in the hospital.

This time, we couldn't even make it on our own to the hospital. Christopher was taken by ambulance, as both his lungs had hyper-extended, and time was everything. Some of the E.R. doctors had questioned this "new medicine" Chris had been on, and it didn't take long for me to figure out what we HAD TO DO! As soon as Chris was home, we went back to our chiropractor, Dr. Dionne, for regular adjustments.

Chris stayed healthy and within a few months swam his way to the top, becoming U.S. Swimming 1996 twelve and under State Champion in both the backstroke and the butterfly. We don't know what the future holds for Chris' health, but we believe in our hearts that chiropractic has helped him. We don't have the answers, but we know where we've been and what we've been through without this help. Seeing Chris doing so well, happy and staying healthy makes me appreciate having gotten to that point which allowed me to stop being skeptical and take a chance on treating Chris' asthma through chiropractic health care. Although it may seem unconventional to treat Chris with adjustments instead of drugs on top of drugs, it no longer matters to me how it seems.

For now, today, and hopefully for tomorrow, chiropractic is somehow working and is giving Chris a better life; a new breath of life through an approach that I'm not going to fight. We're all just too tired of fighting.

Cindy Sullivan Sapp

Dalton's Smile

*You already have the precious mixture that will
make you well. Use it.*

Rumi

The first time I was treated to Dalton's smile, he was
peering over the back fence of my yard with his face
framed in trailing vines of honeysuckle. As we got to be
friends, I learned that he and his two older sisters had
been orphaned and were being raised by their grandparents. Outgoing and well-mannered, the three were a
charming addition to our neighborhood.

Several months later, Dalton accompanied his grandfather, Ernest, to my chiropractic office on an errand, and I
was alarmed to see that his usual sunny smile had grown
timid and uncertain. Uncharacteristically, he hid behind
his grandfather when I spoke to him. His face was pale,
with dark smudges of gray under his eyes. With a quiet
question to Ernest, I asked what was changing this usually
bright, cheerful boy of nine years old into a sad and timid
person. I invited him to allow myself or my husband, Dr.
Pat, to be of any help that might resolve this with Dalton.

I was so personally disturbed with the changes I observed that I couldn't stop thinking of him.

Within a few days, Ernest approached me alone, stating that Dalton had been placed on a drug—to "help him with his school work," and because his attitude had been "poor." With deep concern, he told me that Dalton's lymph nodes had become painfully swollen, and after three progressive referrals to medical doctors, he was even more worried. Ernest said, "All those doctors could tell me was to watch and see if they would 'go down' on their own."

He related his worry about his grandson's poor appetite, his restless sleep patterns and his behavior becoming dull and sluggish. With tears in his own eyes, he asked me, "Do you think you can do something for him, Dr. Sara?"

I explained the Chiropractic Philosophy of Total Body Wellness promoted by our clinic, and outlined a plan of care for Dalton. Using the *Physician's Desk Reference,* I read him the information on the particular medication Dalton was taking, explaining that it would be Ernest's responsibility to approach his medical doctor for advice to gradually reduce, then eventually cease the dosage Dalton was on. I further explained that there was no "simple fix" for Dalton's present condition, and the solution would require long-term efforts. The stresses that Dalton was experiencing, his restlessness, food sensitivities, and sleeplessness could all be improved with chiropractic adjustments, because by normalizing the function of his nervous system, it would facilitate removing interference to his health caused by the Vertebral Subluxation Complex in his spine.

Dalton began his series of weekly visits for adjustments to his spine; and with treatment came the task of teaching him and his family about proper care for his body. We discussed junk foods, food colorings, and artificial flavorings and how they would "make his thinking fuzzy" as well as cause his body to feel "jumpy." I constantly reinforced the teaching that our goal was to achieve *long-term* benefits in his lifestyle, plus aid healing in his body. As he began to heal, he should watch for the real changes in his thinking and concentration, and school would be more fun for him because he could concentrate easier as his body got healthier. So each week we had a brief "chat." He told me how hard he had worked to change that week and what he had learned about his foods saying, "Just because it tastes good, doesn't mean it's good for you, Dr. Sara!" Occasionally, I would answer my front door to find Dalton with a question about some food item he held in his hand.

As the weeks progressed we continued to work as a team; I adjusted the persistent cervical subluxations present and his grandparents stretched their small budget to buy Dalton the clean, quality foods he needed. The progressively colder afternoons would find Dalton in hat, gloves and coat riding his bike for my prescribed "one hour of outside play after school." He didn't know that the sunshine and air were aiding his digestion, and very importantly, promoting the essential *proprioception* stimulating him into better health. We used nutrients to help him assimilate and synthesize proteins and to stimulate more normal brain functioning, promote good sleep habits and handle the normal stresses in his young life. After several months of gradual reduction in dosage, Dalton was drug free!

During one of our adjustments, Ernest said the principal of the school had asked him about Dalton's medication, telling him he didn't think there was any harm in it. Ernest, with his seventh grade education, said, "Well, I just told that principal he hadn't read enough on the subject and he should go to the library and read some books about drugs and kids!" So we gave him copies of studies and articles from our office database to educate Dalton's elementary school principal about the hazards of the drugs doctors are giving kids today.

Gradually, the adjustments in Dalton's neck began to hold. He gained weight and his face began to lose its pale, shadowed look. When he was in conversation with me, he would make direct eye contact and engage me in discussions growing in animation and intelligence. And most importantly, Dalton informed me that he recognized he "felt funny" when he ate certain foods, and didn't like to "mess myself up 'cause the teacher would be all over me, I'd be acting so funny."

In his most recent visit, Dalton's grin lit up the waiting room as he signed in for his weekly adjustment. He plopped his large "Harry Potter" book (700+ pages) onto the counter, then grinned from ear to ear. "Dr. Sara, I have a surprise for you. I got my report card today and my grades have come up thirty-five points! I'm doing so good, I'm on the Honor Roll!"

Sara Aurora Downey, D.C.

Safe—Inside and Out

Every problem has in it the seeds of its own solution. If you don't have any problems, you don't get any seeds . . .

Norman Vincent Peale

I'd been treating a mother and grandmother for several months for injuries they had suffered in an auto accident. They had been struck forcefully from behind, and both had been significantly injured.

In the car with them, had been the woman's four-year-old son, Brandon. Brandon had recovered much more quickly from his injuries, and so I saw him only occasionally as he came intermittently with his mother. One day, as I was working on the mom, she mentioned something about the way Brandon rode in the car since the accident. She said that since that time, he refused to ride facing forward in a seatbelt. Instead, he would only ride looking out the back window, and if any car approached too close, he would begin to scream and cry for her to drive faster so they wouldn't be hit again.

Brandon's mom was concerned, not only for his physical

safety, riding unbelted and facing the wrong way in the car, but also for his emotional well-being. It had been more than six months since the accident and there was no sign of his being able to relax at all while riding in a car. She was afraid that the same feeling of being unsafe in an automobile would spill over into the rest of his life. Brandon was only four years old, and already he lived in terror.

I couldn't ignore her concerns or her pain. Here was another visible injury she had sustained in the accident, and I thought I might be able to fix it; if I had the courage to speak up and risk looking foolish.

I backed into it cautiously, "Have you thought of taking Brandon to a therapist?" I asked.

"No, I haven't," was the reply.

Deep breath, "Well, there's this new technique I know called N.E.T. (Neuro-Emotional Technique) that might help Brandon. Would you trust me enough to give it a try?" I asked.

"Of course, doc. You've done nothing but help us the whole way along. Would you really be willing to do that?" she replied.

"Sure," I said, and swallowed hard.

The most difficult thing about working with Brandon was getting a feel for the muscle test. With a four-year-old, I had to be very sensitive to the feedback of the muscle, but in less than a minute or two I knew I could work with him. Checking his body, it became clear that the emotion it needed to clear was grief; grief over the injury to his family and to his own sense of safety.

I asked, "Brandon, do you remember the car accident?" He nodded.

"Can you remember how sad you felt when it happened?" Again, he nodded.

Asking him just to remember that sadness, I placed his hands on the reflex points that would help clear the emotion and did a gentle spinal correction, then a re-check for more emotions. None showed up. It appeared as though with this one small correction Brandon's body had all it needed to heal, now emotionally as well as physically.

He hopped down off the table, his mom and I exchanged a wondering look, and they left. Later, I got a call telling me that Brandon had gotten into the car and ridden home normally, belted, facing forward—safe inside and out. He's ridden that way ever since.

Jane M. Lock, D.C.

©2003 The New Yorker Collection from cartoonbank.com. All Rights Reserved.

A Mother's First Kiss

We cannot do great things on this earth.
We can only do small things with great love.

Mother Teresa

While in practice, I had the pleasure of seeing many families on a maintenance, or preventive care, basis. One such family of five came in on a regular weekly basis, but never brought their middle child, *Julie. Her mother, *Mary, upon leaving the office one-day, was visibly distraught. Sensitive to the patient's state, my wife and receptionist, Kathy, asked her what was the matter. She broke down crying and told us the story of Julie.

When Julie was sixteen months old, she was given some antibiotics because she was sick with a throat infection. From that point on, she was never the same. She had started to say, "Mommy," "Daddy," "smile," "get up" and "get down." When she was sick, she was listless and had glassy eyes. The medical doctor gave her a heavy dose of antibiotics that seemed to trigger this change to where she became completely withdrawn and said nothing. At times, she was in a constant state of motion, continually running, or in a total deathlike state, just sitting in one spot, staring at nothing, totally oblivious of everyone and everything. Often she would burst out into ferocious temper tantrums where she'd knock everything off the countertops and tables, scream, bite, kick and punch anything or anyone.

"We've had her to every specialist we can think of," Mary said, "and have just been told that she is autistic. We were told to have her institutionalized. We have to break up our family. That is why Julie stays in the car as the family comes into the office in shifts to be adjusted."

Kathy convinced Mary to bring Julie into the office for me to examine. When I entered the room, Julie was screaming and banging her head against the wall, pulling her hair. As I approached her, she began to run. I mirrored every move she made. If she hit the table, I hit the table. As she ran around the room, I ran around the room. If she pulled her hair, I pulled my hair. After three to four minutes of this game play, she stayed still and I was able to touch her. I proceeded to analyze her spine and adjust her, seeing her three times a week. After several weeks, Mary was able to bring Julie into the reception room during regular hours. She would sit and look at the pictures in a book. After ten weeks, the family was in the adjusting room together, all five of them, together again.

I checked and adjusted two of the children. Mary laid face down on the table waiting her turn. I adjusted Julie in my lap then sat her down on the bench. Then I approached Mary for her turn. As I began to palpate Mary's spine, Julie jumped off the bench and came over to Mary, put her arms around her head and kissed it, for the first time. Mary cried out, "Julie you kissed mommy. You kissed me!" and began to cry. We all shed a tear that day.

Three years later I had the pleasure of being invited to Julie's first dance recital.

William C. Remling, D.C., FICA

6

ADDED YEARS

The human spirit is so great a thing that no man can express it; could we rightly comprehend the mind of man nothing would be impossible to us upon the earth.

Paracelsus

A Lesson in Dignity

When Angel came into my office she was very weak and appeared to be near death. She had been given a poor prognosis and was told that nothing could be done to help her. She had difficulty walking and she was stiff and arthritic. Her eyes were clouded with age and had lost their spark. She was unable to talk, and thus could not tell us what she was feeling.

Jane Smith was the one who brought her into my office. She asked if anything could be done to help her. As always, I told her what chiropractic was all about. I explained what a vertebral subluxation was, how it disturbed the nervous system, and how it interfered with the function of the body. I told her that if Angel had subluxations in her spine then I could give her a chiropractic adjustment. I told her that it would help her by contributing to the integrity of the nerve system. I didn't know how much it would help; only time would tell. By the look in Jane's eyes, I knew that it was the first time that she had been given any hope.

As I checked Angel's spine, I found that she was indeed subluxated. I gave her an adjustment. I then told Jane to bring her back a few times a week and we would see how she responded. What followed was nothing short of miraculous. Angel not only got better, she seemed to regain her youth and vibrancy. The spark returned in her ancient eyes. She regained her appetite. As the weeks passed by, she regained her vitality and seemed to turn back the pages of time.

It wasn't long before my staff and I realized that she was a very special patient, one that seemed to warm up the entire office each and every time she came in. Although she couldn't talk to us, you could see the gratefulness and the love in her eyes. She truly loved to come into the office for chiropractic care. It got to where she enjoyed coming in so much, that she didn't want to leave after she received her adjustment. She would just stand there, looking at us with obvious affection while Jane gently tugged on her and told her that it was time to go. You couldn't help but be moved by her presence. Jane said that she never behaved like this anywhere else.

As time went on, Angel experienced several traumas that set her back rather severely. Each time, she bounced back with amazing fortitude. One time, she fell down a flight of stairs after a missed step. Yet, within a few adjustments she was doing well again. Another time she was attacked by a pit bull that jumped out of a passing car, as she was walking down the sidewalk with Jane. When she was brought into the office she was pretty beat up and stiff, but again she bounced right back. Despite these and a few other traumas, Angel responded incredibly well to chiropractic care. Throughout it all, she continued to touch our hearts with her presence and resiliency.

After Angel had been under care for over two years, I received a phone call late one night. It was Jane. She was very upset and told me that something was seriously wrong with Angel. She said that Angel was very weak; would not eat, could not stand up, and seemed worse than ever. I asked Jane if she wanted me to check Angel that night and see if she needed an adjustment. She said no, that Angel had fallen asleep and that she seemed to be resting peacefully. Jane didn't want to wake her.

It was Friday night and I was going out in the morning to make some farm calls to adjust horses. So I told Jane to meet me at the office at 9:00 A.M. and I would check Angel before I went out on my rounds. The next day, as I pulled up to my office, I was surprised to see Angel standing comfortably beside Jane. I asked Jane what had happened. She said that she didn't know, except that Angel had woken up in the morning, and, although a little weak, she looked much better. I checked Angel's spine and gave her an adjustment. Then I gave her a hug and helped her back into Jane's car. As always she gave me that look that I had become so fond of as I said goodbye to her. Jane promised to bring her in after the weekend so I could check her again.

As it turned out, Jane and Angel didn't make it in after the weekend. It wasn't until two weeks later that I found out why. Shortly after our lunch break, the mail arrived and in it was a letter from Jane.

She said that on that day Angel had "a perfect day." It was a sunny day with clear skies. After they had seen me at the office, Jane and Angel went home. Jane made Angel's favorite meal and after lunch they sat out on the front porch and enjoyed the sunshine. For some reason, all of the family just happened to find a reason to stop by for a visit. As the afternoon wore on, it seemed that everyone that Angel loved was somehow able to come by and see her. The only exception was Jane's brother who had moved to the east coast a couple of years earlier and had not been home since. Just as these thoughts were drifting across her mind, Jane noticed a car pull up in front of the house, and out jumped her brother! On an impulse, he had come home for a surprise visit. Angel immediately got up and walked down to meet him. She was obviously glad to see him and vice versa. Jane's brother came quickly up, bent down and gave her a big hug. Angel's day was now completed. She had been blessed with people who had loved her and cared for her throughout her life. Her journey was now at it's end. After Jane's brother greeted her, she laid down, right there. She then quietly went to sleep, and graduated from life.

All of the tumblers of the universe had fallen into place for her that day.

She had been able to say goodbye to everyone that she loved, even her chiropractor. This had a profound impact on my office staff and myself. Since they opened the mail for me, they got the news first. There wasn't a dry eye in the whole bunch. Fortunately, we were able to have a moment alone with our thoughts, because there was suddenly a lull in the flow of patients through the door after we read that letter.

You see, Angel was a chestnut colored Doberman Pinscher.

What she taught me was priceless. It made me realize that perhaps one of the greatest contributions that chiropractic can make is this: it allows our patients to live and die with dignity. It gave Angel over two more years of life that she would not have been able to have otherwise. It allowed her to live out her life with the ones who loved her, and who she loved in return. There were no drugs, no surgery, and no euthanasia. There were only chiropractic adjustments releasing tiny rivulets of life force allowing life to express itself without interference. When the time came for her to graduate from life, she was able to do so gently and with amazing grace.

I am grateful and truly honored to have known her and to have been a part of her life.

Randy Baze, D.C.

"I need to have you just relax
and trust me on this, Mrs. Hostrander."

CLOSE TO HOME. ©*John McPherson. Reprinted with permission of UNIVERSAL PRESS
SYNDICATE. All rights reserved.*

"Face" Restored

While there's life, there's hope.

Marcus Tullius Cicero

Helen,* 74 years old, had been a chiropractic patient for a number of years and was in good health, active and vital in the community. She and her husband decided to move to a larger town before they got any older in case they would need services not available in our little town . . . hospital facilities, public transportation, etc., so they moved near Wal-Mart. We had not seen her in about six months, when one morning we received a phone call from Helen. She was very upset and was very difficult to understand. It was obvious to me something was affecting her speech and ability to pronounce words, besides just being distraught. I feared she'd had a light stroke or similar episode. But she'd seen a medical doctor at a minor emergency care facility already and he'd sent her home with a prescription for Valium to settle her down, saying there was nothing else to be done.

Her husband drove her out to our clinic later that morning. Even though it was chilly outside, she was bundled up with a scarf over her head and a muffler around her face as if it was twenty degrees below zero. As she began to take off her scarf and muffler, I could see her hair was a mess, she wore no make-up, had been crying and then she turned to me full face. The right side of her lovely, porcelain skinned, barely-lined face, had literally "fallen." Her eye drooped, her cheek sagged terribly and her mouth was drawn down. She looked so pitiful. My husband took her back to the exam room immediately, then came right back within a few minutes. I expected him to say, "Call an ambulance," but, he said, "Reschedule the rest of the morning, explain we have an emergency, I won't have time to see anyone else."

Helen was walking just fine and I had noted she signed the patient register in her usual neat penmanship. Other than her face, she appeared physically as normal as ever. I heard in muffled tones, him asking her several questions, asking "what?" and "pardon me?" several times, and taking her blood pressure at several intervals. He then took some new x-rays on her, putting her on the intersegmental traction table to relax her while he developed the x-rays. Then they went back into the exam and adjusting room. I thought, *What in the world is he going to be able to do?* Yes, he was great at applied kinesiology techniques and acupressure, but I could never have guessed at what I would see about an hour later.

My husband came out to the front desk and told me to find an appointment time for Helen the next morning. Between the exam room and the front desk, we had a mirror where patients could rearrange their clothes after their treatment, blot their make-up, or straighten up their hair. The phone rang, and I turned to answer. When I turned back toward the exam room Helen had come out to the mirror and was quietly sobbing. I opened the door to let her husband in and went to hand her a tissue. Her husband gasped as he looked in the mirror. So I dared a glance . . . and gasped myself!

Helen was smiling and crying at the same time. Her face looked essentially normal with exception of a slight turn-down of the corner of her mouth. One would have never known she'd had an attack of Bell's Palsy.

Helen enjoyed a full recovery, and she had a wonderful time prancing back into the minor emergency clinic and showing the young medical doctor what her chiropractor had done for her. Even though it was an eighty-mile roundtrip journey for this senior couple, Helen came every month for an adjustment until last year, when she passed peacefully in her sleep in her home.

Eva Wallert

Let's Give it a Shot

Our human bodies are miracles, not because they defy laws of nature, but precisely because they obey them.

Harold S. Kushner

I was a chiropractic intern in the heart of Los Angeles. I couldn't wait for my first patient to walk through the clinic doors. After three years of graduate study, and countless weekend seminars learning the procedures with which to eliminate a patient's neck, back or head pain, I was ready for my first doctor/patient experience.

He walked through the door in the form of a frail seventy-two-year-old gentleman. On the intake form he had checked virtually every symptom box; back pain, neck pain, sinusitis, allergies, digestive disorder, headaches, numbness, tingling, and on and on. My very first patient was not looking as if it would be a very simple case.

Throughout the course of my consultation, my enthused spirits were dampened by the reality of the severity of his spinal damage. He softly and laboriously explained how he had visited specialist after specialist, searching for the answer to his suffering. His frustration with his condition was literally draining the life from him. After analyzing his x-rays, which showed severe degeneration, late phase arthritic changes, and massive compensatory structuring within his spinal column, he spoke succinctly again. With a voice spoken as if his life's hope depended on the answer, he asked, "Can you help me?"

I answered honestly, "I have no idea how your body will respond. All I know is that your spine is subluxated in the areas I have shown you and your body will respond better if it is un-subluxated."

Speaking without much confidence he said, "Well, I've tried everything else, we may as well give this a shot." I then adjusted him and scheduled him for his second adjustment the very next day.

I was waiting in the hallway of the clinic when he returned the next day. He shuffled quickly past me, barely glancing at me, and saying, "Dr. Danielson, I need to speak with you." Being my first patient, and knowing his spinal condition, I immediately thought the worst. As I followed him to the adjusting room, I had to consciously place my feet one in front of the other because my legs had turned to rubber with fear and anxiety. Entering the room, we took our seats and I apprehensively asked him, "What's wrong, my friend?" Taking a deep breath, he emphatically announced, "Last night I had the largest erection of my life." The silence was deafening. Words were not coming to me, so he continued, "My wife thanks you." By now I had turned a deep shade of red and wanted to change to a more comfortable subject. "How is your back and neck feeling today?" I asked. Instantly he replied, "Who cares!"

This gentle old man had not had an erection for over eight years. He went on to explain how this had affected his life and nearly ruined his forty-nine-year marriage. He now had hope that not only this area of his life would continue to improve, but also the other infirmities for which he originally consulted me.

Over the next year, I continued to help him and he did improve greatly, however, his improvement was limited by his massive spinal deformity. I thank God for this man's presence in my practice because in my first doctor/patient relationship, he taught me something that all chiropractors learn at some point in their careers. And that is that ALL tissues, organs, and cells are controlled by the nervous system. Whether it's visual acuity or hearing on one end, to bowel and sexual function on the other.

Jeffrey Danielson, D.C.

Nana and Gump

*Within you right now is the power to do things
you never dreamed possible. This power becomes
available to you just as soon as you can change
your beliefs.*

Maxwell Maltz

In 1946, a tragic accident happened to my great-grandfather that would bless and change the lives of his descen-
dants for many generations to come.

My great-grandmother and great-grandfather, who we
affectionately call "Nana" and "Gump," were some of the
early pioneers in southwestern Alberta, Canada. Through
much hard work and sacrifice, they were able to obtain a
farm near the small town of Magrath. Things started going
well for them in 1940, and they were finally making money
by growing crops and raising cattle.

In the spring of 1946, Gump bought a new light-delivery
truck and began to seed thirty acres of peas. While seed-
ing one day, Gump started having some chest pains. They
became so severe that he could not sleep at night. When
he arose in the morning and moved around, the pain

would ease a little, but at night it would start again. One morning, on his way back from town, Gump passed out and the truck he was driving spun out of control and hit a large tree in the ditch. When he was found, he was taken into the local hospital where the doctor proceeded to put on a full-body cast without taking any x-rays.

When Gump regained consciousness he was in so much pain that Nana phoned a doctor in another city for a second opinion. The doctor assessed the situation and put Gump immediately on an airplane to a larger hospital in the capital city of Edmonton. Gump had the best neurosurgeon in North America at that time working with him. The first thing they did was remove the cast and take some x-rays. They discovered that Gump had a broken back, a spinal cord that was nearly severed, and his pelvis was cracked across the lower back. Gump was completely paralyzed, having only control over the movement of his eyes. The doctor told him that he might not live, but Gump survived six weeks and stabilized enough to be released from the hospital. His prognosis was that he would never be able to walk again.

At one point, the doctor asked Nana if she believed in nutrition as a means of helping to heal the body. He advised her to go to the health food store and buy a good book on nutrition and study it, as it would do more to help Gump than any other thing. She did exactly as the doctor advised and made health food study and practice an integral part of their life from then on.

Back on the farm, a bed was moved into the living room for easier care, and the community rallied together to provide help to the family. Many people came by to help. One day, a friend brought over a man that had some chiropractic training to see if he could help. He began some treatments, and finally, after a year's time, Gump could feel a little life creeping into his limbs. Eventually, the muscles started to redevelop. One of his nephews built a steel frame to go over the bed, with straps and chains to help him pull himself up. With Nana's tender care, he began to feel alive again.

The first time they took him out of bed, one man on each side holding him up, his legs were just like jelly and crumbled when they would touch the floor. But after many tries, he could feel a little strength coming. After a year, he was able to walk a little with crutches and with a lot of help.

After several bouts of pneumonia, the doctor advised the family that he should be taken to a warmer climate for the winter, and so, by October 1948, they were ready to leave for Arizona—the land of pure sunshine.

While in Arizona, they had many people try different therapies by working on his body. They did not notice much improvement and Gump was still quite paralyzed. Finally, they located someone with chiropractic training and again he began receiving regular adjustments. Gump's condition began to improve and by the end of the winter they returned home to Alberta. He continued to travel to Calgary to a chiropractor, and within a few years he returned to his work as a farmer and was able to support his family for another twenty years. He lived to be eighty-years-old. Gump remained somewhat crippled in his hands, and had difficulty walking, but through chiropractic care, good nutrition, exercise and his own determination, he had a full, rewarding life and left a great legacy to his children.

From this tragic experience and near miraculous recovery, many generations of our family have been deeply influenced. Gump's two sons continued on with their education and both became doctors of chiropractic. In the next generation, Gump had ten grandchildren who went on to become chiropractors. In the fourth generation, so far there are two great-grandchildren enrolled in chiropractic college and three more preparing for admission. The legacy of chiropractic, its philosophy, its practice, and its healing influence will be part of our family for many generations to come.

Randal Cooper

Casey's First Adjustment

The best and safest thing is to keep a balance in your life, acknowledge the great powers around us and in us. If you can do that, and live that way, you are really a wise man.

Euripides

My dog Casey has been a companion for more than thirteen years now. In that time, I have watched this small creature transform from an obnoxiously active and energetic puppy into an elderly, wise spirit dressed in a dog suit.

Since she was about the age of three, Casey and I have struggled with her allergies. Between her chewing, licking and itching, I'm not sure which one of us was crazier. After trying several conservative forms of treatment without relief, we resorted to the use of prednisone. It worked. Unfortunately, prednisone does not come without side effects. Off and on for years now, prednisone has been both a friend and foe for Casey. While keeping her allergies manageable, she's developed cataracts and become increasingly arthritic. I'd like to say she has aged gracefully, but the long-term use of prednisone has hastened the process.

A steadfast weak point for Casey has always been that box of treats in the pantry. Believe me, she has trained me well in the knowledge of rewards for good deeds. One evening, after 'taking care of business,' Casey came inside expecting that reward. Excitedly, she jumped up, standing on her hind legs only to let out a shriek of pain. Not realizing what had just occurred, she repeated the same maneuver only to produce the same result. This time she understood and responded to the pain. She forgot about the treats. My dog was hurt.

By now, I was five years into my chiropractic career, confident of my skills in treating humans . . . not so confident with animals, even one that meant so much to me. Professionally, I knew I was dealing with the frailty of an eighty-year-old in human years. Emotionally, I wanted to do everything and anything possible to help my canine companion.

Within an hour, she was unwilling to climb steps, walked anguishly, and lost interest in any of the activity going on around the house. I cautiously and hesitantly checked her spine. I was suspicious of two particular bones, one in her neck and the other in her mid-back. She winced every time I touched those bones. It was her best effort at telling me what was wrong, but my analytical side wanted more certainty.

Casey and I made a visit to the vet the next morning. He knew Casey's background with prednisone, as well as the fact that I was a chiropractor. I explained the scenario to him and he performed his exam and confirmed my findings. We discussed the options, one of them being a chiropractic adjustment. Although it wasn't at the top of his list, he understood my desire to not medicate her anymore. One hour later, a colleague and I adjusted Casey.

Three hours later, my dog was walking normally and climbing stairs. Her personality returned. My dog was back.

Since that time, she has had no reoccurrences and we've gotten her completely off prednisone. She now takes a homeopathic remedy for her allergies, and natural supplementation for her arthritis. She is more alert than she has been in years.

In that moment of pain, I saw my dog's quality of life slipping away . . . because of that moment she has more life than expected.

My dog reaffirmed my belief in chiropractic care and the 'rewards' of an adjustment. Everyone needs care, even the four-legged ones. . .

"Hey Casey, wanna treat?"

Brenda Pfeiffer, D.C.

7

BEYOND THE CALL OF DUTY

Always do more than is required of you.

George S. Patton

Adjusting to a Better Life

I had only been in practice about a year when I first met Mrs. Hoffman. She was recently divorced and working as a waitress to support her children. During our initial consultation, she complained of back pain and said that her back started hurting when she was lifting heavy trays of food. I explained that I adjusted the spine to help the overall body operate at its peak efficiency; not directly to alleviate back pain, but to correct any nerve interference I found.

Mrs. Hoffman also asked if I thought I could help her son, Richie, who was "in really bad shape." I said I could usually help, "if the patient is alive and has a nerve system." Hope was reflected in her eyes.

Richie was one of seven-year-old twin boys. His brother, Johnny, was just fine, healthy and active. Richie, however, was a different story. He was dying. Seventeen different doctors had seen him and not one of them could agree on a diagnosis. In seven years, over thirty-seven different medications had been prescribed for him. He was in the hospital twice for tests and observation. Each time, his stay had been extended and the family's insurance had paid tens of thousands of dollars for Richie's medical expenses. The last time he was hospitalized, the baffled doctors felt Richie's condition was hopeless and sent him home with instructions that his mother should make him as comfortable as possible until his death. Currently, Richie was taking five different medications, including the drug Phenobarbital, which is used to control seizures.

Mrs. Hoffman received this dire verdict about a week before she came to see me for her back pain.

After listening to her story, I told her I would examine Richie for nerve interference and she was not to worry about payment. I referred to the sign in our waiting room that said, "We accept all patients regardless of their condition or financial ability to pay."

When I saw Richie, I must admit I was quite shocked by his physical condition. Mrs. Hoffman had to carry him in her arms into my office. Because of his condition, he had never been able to wear shoes and was dressed only in shorts and a t-shirt. He seemed to have no body or facial hair and his frail body was covered with sores from head to toe. On his legs, the sores were so profuse that I couldn't see any healthy skin. Furthermore, he was so drugged from the five different medications he was taking that his eyes were rolling back in his head. Richie really looked closer to death than anyone I had ever seen. His brother, Johnny, had come with them and the contrast between the two children made Richie's situation all the more dramatic.

It was difficult to examine the boy. I was so moved by his condition, I actually had to leave the examining room to regain my composure. When I returned and examined him, I explained to his mother that Richie had nerve interference in his neck. I told her I would adjust him every day for awhile. I went so far as to tell her that if Richie were my child, I would slowly try to reduce his medications.

We agreed that I would adjust Mrs. Hoffman and both her

sons for five dollars a week. I had also found nerve interference in Johnny's spine, even though he said he felt great. I wanted to adjust him before he developed symptoms.

After I'd been working with the family for about six weeks, I began to get discouraged. I didn't see any real change in Richie's condition and I wondered if his mother noticed this too, and felt disappointed.

When I questioned her as to whether or not she thought the adjustments were helping, I have never forgotten what she said to me. I was a young doctor then, but many years later, I still carry her message of faith with me. Mrs. Hoffman said:

"When I first came to you, I also suffered with severe headaches and menstrual cramps I never told you about. I was taking a lot of medication, which I now no longer need. I felt great except for my back, but it seems improved. You explained how the power that made my body is the only power that could heal it, and I knew you were talking about God. I understand that it may be too late for Richie because he's been sick so long, but, if you give up on him, I have no other place to go for help. Your adjustments have already helped me so much, I just know that if it's God's will for Richie to recover, then he is going to get better. Please don't give up."

How could I do anything but agree to continue the adjustments? I cast aside my own discouragement and lack of faith and made a promise to myself that I would never again doubt the ability of my adjustments, or the hope they offered.

The very next week, the miracle began to unfold. Richie's mother excitedly showed me some areas of clear skin where earlier there had only been open, bloody sores. She had gradually reduced his medication. The child continued to make progress, and, at the end of eight weeks of care, it was obvious that his body was healing at an amazing rate. He was excited about the hair fuzz growing on top of his head. Furthermore, he was walking into my office now, and he was proudly wearing his first pair of shoes.

It took several more months for Richie to be completely healed. Finally, the only reminders of his condition were areas of skin that were marked with a pinkish coloration where the open sores had been.

I never found out the correct name for Richie's medical condition because none of the experts could agree on a diagnosis. The only thing Mrs. Hoffman and I cared about was that Richie got his life back. It was stunning proof that with an improved spinal structure, the potential for a healthy body and normal function can return.

And, I will always be grateful for the lesson I learned about not giving up on any patient, regardless of his or her disease.

Terry A. Rondberg, D.C.

A Dog Named Sparky

Here is the simple but powerful rule . . . always give people more than they expect to get.

Nelson Boswell

It was a warm spring afternoon in Texas when a young lady called me about her pet dog named Sparky. I have been a veterinarian for the past twenty-two years, but had the priviledge to teach, in a chiropractic college, a few of their basic science courses. Sparky was a twelve-year-old male cocker spaniel that had been diagnosed with epileptic seizures. He had been seen by three different veterinarians in an attempt to bring the seizures under control. The owner was now contacting me as a last resort before she had Sparky put to sleep. She told me she heard I could do something to his spine that might help him, and, since it was a last resort, she was willing to try anything. His seizures were not under control despite the fact he was taking several anti-seizure drugs on a daily basis. I agreed to see him, but I told her I did not know if I could help him or not.

On the day she brought Sparky to me, it had turned

cold and was raining. Sparky could not walk very well and she allowed him to just walk into my clinic off of his leash. His gait was very stiff and his movement was severely limited. I greeted the owner and then reached down to pet Sparky's head. When I did, he fell to the floor, rolled on his back and began to shake violently. The owner said, "There, he is going through one of his seizures." I observed Sparky until he stopped, but in all of my experience as a veterinarian, I had never seen a seizure like this and I had my doubts if, in fact, it was a true seizure. I picked Sparky up and set him on the examination table. I began my exam, as I always do, from the head and worked back toward the tail. The most obvious thing I noticed was how tight the muscles of Sparky's neck were. He stood with his shoulders hunched up toward his head and he had almost no mobility to his neck. It was as if you raised your shoulders up under your ears, and when you turned sideways, you turned your whole upper body.

This is how Sparky moved whenever he walked. Sparky would cringe and whimper whenever I touched his neck muscles, and he resisted and cried when I tried to move his head or neck. At that time, I had little experience in palpating spines for the signs of subluxations, but even my fledgling fingers could feel that Sparky had a severely misplaced or subluxated atlas. The right side of Sparky's atlas felt like it was much higher than the left side, and when I touched it Sparky would really whimper.

Since I was new at this adjusting stuff, I had no clue how to adjust this vertebrae, or how high or low to set the Activator® instrument I was going to use, so I just guessed. I took the instrument and figured since the atlas was so demonstrably out of place, I would set it on its highest setting. I placed the tip of the instrument firmly on Sparky's neck over the right lateral (side) transverse process of the atlas. I fired the instrument and there was a tremendous "pop" sound and all four of Sparky's legs splayed out to the side and he fell with a thud onto the table. The owner gasped and looked at me with an accusatory, puzzled look.

Let me digress for a moment. In veterinary school, as in all professional schools, they teach you to maintain your cool under pressure and never reveal your feelings through your physiognomy. In order to maintain the patient's confidence, you should never look scared or confused when performing a procedure, although many times one may experience these feelings.

Sparky's owner was searching my face for even the slightest look that might indicate that I did not know what I was doing. I maintained my cool even though in my mind I thought I had broken Sparky's neck. Because of the way he collapsed, I thought I had killed him! I was scared. Here it was, the very first time I had ever adjusted an animal, the very first time I had ever used the Activator® instrument, and I thought I had killed my patient, or at the very least, broken his neck and paralyzed him.

For what seemed like an eternity, Sparky lay there on his belly on the table. Then ever so slowly, he began to pull his legs under him and stood up! Inside, I was jumping with joy. Yea! He was breathing (which meant that he was probably not dead), and he could stand (which meant that his neck was probably not broken). I quickly picked him up and set him on the floor to see if he could walk. The first thing he did was shake from his head down to his tail. The kind of a shake a dog does when they get out of the water to shake the water off of their fur. He shook his head back and forth, and slapped his long floppy ears against the side of his head. I was ecstatic as he seemed to be okay. The owner was crying with joy. She said she had not seen him shake his head and body like that in years. Sparky looked up at me and actually smiled. He could move his head and he walked with much greater freedom of movement. He actually trotted out of my office.

I told the owner I wanted to see Sparky the next week for another adjustment. I thought long and hard about Sparky and what had actually happened that day that I adjusted his neck. Sparky had a severely subluxated atlas that had caused profound muscle spasms in his neck and shoulders.

He was in pain, and when people would reach down to pet his head he would fall on the floor and quiver in pain. This behavior was being misdiagnosed as a seizure.

When his owner returned for the one-week follow-up treatment, she told me what I expected to hear; Sparky was a different dog. He was able to do all those things he had been able to do as a puppy. He was running and playing and eating and being a dog again!

I adjusted Sparky twice more after that first visit. Each time, he was doing better and better. It amazed the veterinarian in me the difference I was able to make in Sparky's and his owner's life.

Eventually Sparky passed away from liver cancer, but it was many years later. He lived out the rest of his life as a happy, carefree, Cocker Spaniel that loved to run through fields and chase balls. The owner was so impressed with the success that chiropractic treatments had on her dog, that she actually enrolled in Chiropractic College to pursue a career as a chiropractor.

Gene Giggleman, D.V.M.

[EDITOR'S NOTE: *For more information concerning chiropractic for animals, please contact Gene Giggleman, D.V.M at Parker College of chiropractic or at* ggiglman@parkercc.edu.]

The Calling

*You have powers you never dreamed of. You
can do things you never thought you could do.
There are no limitations in what you can do
except the limitations of your own mind . . .*

Darwin P. Kingsley

I have volunteered at the non-profit Oklahaven
Children's Chiropractic Center, which has been maintained by private donations, without the aid of state or
federal governments, for seven years. Most look at me
incredulously when I tell them of the miracles we see here.
As the Chiropractic Assistant/Public Relations/
Development person, I have witnessed so many miracles!

Once there was an infant who was so physically mal-
formed and brain injured that I went home after his first
visit and cried. As I prayed, I wondered if it was really possible that he too could be helped. The next day, following
a chiropractic treatment, his nurse quietly held and
observed him. As I sat at my desk, I heard her say, "I ain't
believing this!"

My heart began to race as I wondered what could have

happened. As I waited to see what would transpire, she repeated very loudly, "I ain't believing this!"

As I walked toward the room she added, "His ears are curling!" I entered the "giraffe" treatment room (all of our rooms are named after animals and identified by wall murals), and it was clear that he was changing. His auricle, or outer edge of the ear, was curling, showing a greater definition toward a more normal structure. We observed that the child was not visually tracking outlines, responding to his mother's simple commands. He was turning his head and tracking our voices as well. The nurse said, "And to think I thought his parents were crazy for bringing him for chiropractic treatment, especially for taking him half way across the country to Oklahoma City!"

To this nurse, who had worked with this baby for six months on a daily basis, his subtle changes were obvious. She was able to notice the smallest improvements as his body gradually restored function.

The Center has been instrumental in aiding the parents to develop an eye for these subtle changes. I have watched the Parent Support Group become an invaluable tool to educate parents to share, address and understand their fears about their children's conditions. They accomplish this by implementing positive changes in the family's diet, reinforcing the importance of daily treatment, and a need for a drug-free, natural lifestyle. I have seen parents use these tools to help their children reach their maximum potential, even the profoundly brain-injured children. The parents learn to see the wellness in their children. Experience has taught me that many children require more intensive and frequent treatments than others.

Some ask why I choose to work with children whom others have said to institutionalize and forget. My heart cries for these parents. As a parent myself, I find it appalling. Here at the Center, I have the privilege of helping them unfold into healthier, happier children. This is the place where I observe and share in life-changing miracles no one had before dared to anticipate; one miracle after another. That is why I am here. Why would I choose employment elsewhere?

Ginger Hotard Humphries

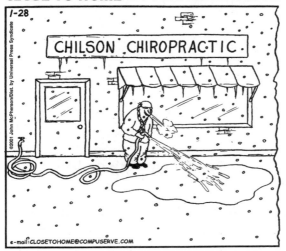

When Chiropractors go bad

CLOSE TO HOME. ©*John McPherson. Reprinted with permission of UNIVERSAL PRESS SYNDICATE. All rights reserved.*

A Hidden Miracle

During my last year at chiropractic school, I was privileged to be included in a chiropractic mission to El Salvador. I joined a group of fifty dedicated chiropractors and interns for a weeklong trip. In small groups, we spread out all over the country to bring chiropractic to the people of El Salvador. My small group was stationed at a church in the capital, San Salvador.

The first morning, we arrived just before 8:00 A.M. to see 100 people lined up outside of the church. Some had traveled for more than four hours by bus. Through word of mouth and news reports, they had heard of our arrival and anxiously waited to be seen by the American chiropractors.

Seven of us quickly set up our adjusting tables in a small room just inside of the church. As the clock struck 8:00 A.M., the outside doors opened and the line rushed forward. It was first come, first serve and as soon as one patient finished, the next in line was just seconds away. Being a chiropractic intern, I was used to seeing only a few patients per day. I quickly adapted my skills to be able to see over 100 patients per day. The range of conditions, illnesses, and complaints was amazing. There was everything from severe scoliosis and back injuries, to heart problems and diabetes.

Many patients touched my heart during my time in El Salvador, but the most memorable was Miguel. About half way through the first morning, a mother brought her six-year-old son to me. My Spanish was very limited, but with the help of a translator I understood the boy to have a very weak immune system. He had frequent head and chest colds, sinus infections and bronchitis. His mother was very concerned about him since he was continually sick.

After examining the boy, I discovered he had severe misalignment of one of the vertebrae in his upper neck. I adjusted him that morning. I explained to his mother that we were only here for a week and it was vitally important that he be adjusted as often as possible. She agreed to bring him back for his second adjustment that afternoon and then every day that week.

The next day I kept my eye out for him. I didn't see him in the morning, but I saw him just after lunch. He had a big smile on his face and was very excited to be back. I checked him again and found some improvement since the previous day. Encouraged by the changes, I made another adjustment in his upper neck.

On the third day, I was again thrilled to see Miguel and his mother. Not only did Miguel have a huge smile on his face, this time so did his mother. She was elated and was talking so quickly in Spanish that my translator could hardly keep up. I understood about Miguel's illnesses, but I did not know about his other challenges. His mother explained that Miguel had difficulty talking because he had problems making certain sounds and articulating his words. He had previously been shy and withdrawn due to his difficulty communicating. Miguel's mother was so excited because suddenly Miguel's ability to communicate completely changed. He began talking as a normal six-year-old boy would. He was able to form sounds properly and articulate his words. Miguel could express himself and tell stories and be the young boy he was meant to be.

I will never forget Miguel, nor the precious week I spent serving in El Salvador. It was an honor and a privilege to be part of that mission. Everyone greeted me with a warm heart and open arms. They are some of the most loving and gracious people I have ever met. I left El Salvador not only with memories that will touch my heart forever, but also a bag filled with gifts from many of the patients as a thank you for bringing chiropractic into their lives. Every time I think of Miguel it reminds me that there is a hidden miracle in all of us just waiting to be uncovered.

Laura L. Peterson, D.C.

Gangster to Graduate

The man who graduates today and stops learning tomorrow is uneducated the day after.

Newton D. Baker

I first met John about four years ago. He came to my office with a low back injury he had suffered while on the job. His treatment period would prove to be lengthy and as time passed, I began to learn about the real John. He had moved to Texas from the gangs of Chicago with his wife, whom he fondly referred to as "the old lady," and their two children. He has often told the story of why he left Chicago, and I remember his vivid descriptions of gang life and how he barely escaped with his own life on several occasions.

He had dropped out of school with no plans of ever returning, accepting this as his fate in life. In time, I began to realize that John was more than just a street wise man; he had learned something before he quit school. I really believed that John owed it to himself and his family to give school another chance. In many of our sessions, I would ask John if he had considered returning for a GED, and maybe attending college someday. He would always quickly respond by saying, "Never, I am just too old."

Call it cliché, but I believe that you are never too old to learn something new. He just didn't have anyone to encourage him. I remember how he impressed me with his quick wit and intellect, and often remarked to him that I thought it was a shame he would not consider at least getting his GED.

When John moved further into chiropractic treatment, many others in my clinic began to see potential in John too. They quickly jumped on the GED encouragement wagon. Once, just before he left, he turned to me and said, "Thanks."

As usual, I said, "Glad I could help you today," and to my surprise, he said, "No doctor, for more than that . . . for the encouragement." John then invited me to go with him to get his diploma. He had passed his high school equivalency exam. I was quite shocked, and honored. All of those pep talks had worked. John admitted to me that he did not want to be another drop-out statistic. I was very proud of him, and of myself for getting to know my patients and making a difference in their lives.

As his treatment progressed, John found a better job that paid more money. He had a high school diploma and the world at his feet. I hoped that all the encouragement my staff and I had given him would push him to the next level and that he would consider a college education. Though I thought my efforts would be fruitless, it was something positive to dream about. Well, it wasn't long before John finished his treatments and was released from my care. I would never know the fate of my patient John. But, I had tried.

It wasn't until some months later that I had a surprise visitor at my clinic. He would not give his name. As I walked out to the lobby, I saw a familiar face. It was John and he was holding some sort of invoice. I walked out to greet him and asked how I could help him. He said he didn't want to stay long he just wanted to thank me. I was not accustomed to patients coming back to thank me with a bill in their hand, so as I looked at him oddly, I said the usual, "No problem and glad to do it." Then he said, "No doctor, you don't understand, this is a tuition payment for college . . . for me to attend college."

Sheryl L. Tollenaar, D.C.

Adding Life to Life

A gentleman came into my office who seemed otherwise like every other fifty-year-old man with a sacroiliac problem. What made this man different were the interesting questions he asked me about how much weight my adjusting tables could bear, and what was the heaviest patient I had ever treated. The answers were 500 and 400 pounds, respectively.

These, and many other questions, I learned, were originated by his wife, Janice. Janice entered my life weighing 323 pounds. She was taking eleven prescription medications and an average of thirty Advil® tablets a day to manage headaches. She had undergone a number of surgeries in her lifetime, including back surgery, and was scheduled for neck surgery. Her hope in coming to my office was to reduce her Advil® intake to ten a day or less in preparation for the impending surgery.

Janice was, and remains, the most unique patient I have ever seen. One of her unique features was her willingness to take personal responsibility for her health. She took extensive notes and typed them up for me. Her notes were her responses to the treatment I gave her and a record of other doctor visits and her prescriptions.

At the time Janice entered my office, she had about a four-hour period of function during the course of the day. Her husband and two teenage children provided much of the assistance she needed. But in a very short time, Janice began to realize the possibilities that awaited her with treatment.

Within a week she achieved her original goal of reduced Advil® intake. Due to her very positive response to adjustments, her goals quickly changed. Within months of beginning treatment, she was completely off all but two prescriptions, decided to cancel her surgery, and changed her diet and exercise habits.

The medical doctors who were managing her care told Janice that her life expectancy was compromised and that she would need multiple surgeries to prolong her life. Janice decided to make me, her chiropractor, her primary doctor. Even though her insurance would not accept the change, she committed to follow my counsel.

Janice lost more than 150 pounds and she was able to function more than sixteen hours a day every day. She was then diagnosed with non-Hodgkin's lymphoma. Although traditional medicine recommended chemotherapy and radiation, she elected to follow a more conservative approach through chiropractic, nutrition and positive thinking. That was five years ago. Since then, Janice's health is better than ever. In her own words, she is "healthier now than I have ever been in my entire life."

Chiropractic has dramatically changed her life. In Janice's own words, "Chiropractic has saved my life."

Janice now has a life of good health and an expectancy of many years to grow old with her children and unborn grandchildren.

John Holland, D.C.

8

DEFINING
MOMENTS

*Discoveries are often made by not following
instructions, by going off the main road, by
trying the untried.*

Frank Tyger

You're No Doctor . . .

It was the Spring of 1977. The previous October, I graduated, at last, a doctor of chiropractic. After interning briefly, I finally opened my own office and then the long waiting began. When will the phone ring, when will the patients begin to pour into my "miracle care center," as I secretly referred to it?

Then one day, in walks the long awaited patient. He was an interesting patient with the stereotypical aches and pains that one would expect of a chiropractic patient. But I would soon learn that Charlie was anything but typical.

When Charlie was a young man he enlisted in the military during WWII. Prior to enlisting, Charlie was an accomplished prizefighter with many titles to his name. Instead of going off to Europe to fight in the war, Charlie fought in the ring as an enlisted soldier. Charlie explained to me that, "Even in times of war, soldiers still need entertainment and I was happy to provide it."

After a thorough examination of his spine and nervous system, he was x-rayed. I was horrified! I thought x-ray findings like those were only in textbooks. His spine appeared to be that of an old man that had fallen on his head one too many times.

On a subsequent visit, I began to explain my findings to Charlie and the potential seriousness this posed to his long-term health. Without batting an eye, Charlie said to me, "Are we going to talk about it all day or are you going to fix it?" With that, I began to treat Charlie.

On a typical office visit, Charlie would be seated in a chair facing the door waiting to see me. As soon as I opened that door to enter he would then liken that to the bell ringing at the beginning of a round. The better Charlie felt the quicker he jumped to his feet, dancing as if he were Rocky Marciano in the ring, and guess who the opponent was? Yours truly. Charlie would dance with his two fists clenched and both arms protecting his body. Charlie would say, "Put 'em up doc, lets go a few rounds." Charlie would come at me with his body gyrating and swings coming within millimeters of my jaw. One day, he asked me if he could show me a few moves, and I made the mistake of taking the bait. This was equivalent to putting a mouse in front of a cat. If he would have let that left uppercut go, I probably wouldn't be here today.

Almost twenty years went by and we became very close. He would come in for his regular preventative adjustments like clock work. Then one day he called and cancelled his visit. Weeks and months went by and no Charlie. Finally, I decided to check in on him with a call at home. "Hi doc," he answered, "I've got some new health problems and my family wants me to go to a 'real doctor' for a check up." Well, the second opinion was not an issue with me but the 'real doctor' comment was as if Charlie had sucker punched me. "I'll call when I want to come in," was his final reply. I thought to myself, *That was a low blow.*

After regular visits for over a twenty-year period, and suddenly, no more Charlie. I wouldn't see Charlie again for over two years. Often I would wonder how he was, but time has a way of helping your thoughts move on. I really missed him, for he and I became very close. Perhaps we just enjoyed sparring together, after this amount of time, I actually got a little cocky.

One busy afternoon, as I moved from one adjustment room to the next, I saw an image of a person holding onto a walker at the front of the office. To this day I don't know what moved me to peek into the reception room; I had never done that before. I just had to know who that person was. To my surprise, it was my old friend Charlie. I'm sure my facial expression was that of shock. There stood in front of me an unkept feeble old soul, soiled pants, mismatched buttons and buttonholes, unshaven, struggling to remain standing.

"Charlie!" I exclaimed.

"Doc, " he replied.

With a reception room full of patients, I ran out to greet him. It was as if no one was there, only my friend and I. Charlie shared how, over the past two years, medical treatment had not helped. The countless specialists, numerous prescription drugs and the hospital stays were of no sucess.

"I didn't think I was going to make it," he said.

I asked Charlie what the doctors said, and his reply was, "You know, Doc, those bastards were trying to kill me. They told my family that I was plain old." He went on, further stating that his family wanted to move him out of his home and put him in, as he called it, "one of those old-fart homes where you go to die."

I don't think there was a dry eye in the office as Charlie went on to say, "Doc, I knew if anyone could help me, I knew it would be you." I don't think all the training in the world could have prepared me for that moment.

Once again I began treating Charlie, except this time it was different. Each time I opened the door Charlie would sit there slumped over the walker with his arms under his chest. I wish I could tell you I had all the confidence in the world in my abilities, but I didn't. Some days I didn't think I could help him, and then I heard a familiar whisper deep inside of my being, reminding me of my early years at college. It was Dr. Galen Price, my philosophy professor. I remember his words as if spoken today, *"It is not you, the chiropractor, that heals, but that intelligence with each and every human that does the healing. You cure nothing."* He went on to explain, *"The power that made the body, heals the body. Don't play God, just adjust them and innate will take over from there; and never, ever give up on a patient."*

I continued to treat Charlie. Some days there seemed to be a hint of improvement, then back sliding. Finally the day came when Charlie started to push the walker with purpose, as if to say, "Get out of my way, I'm in a hurry." Several weeks later he had no walker, only a cane. Charlie would say, "A few more weeks Doc and I'll be ready to go a few rounds with you." I agreed, now hopeful.

Then it happened. I opened the door . . . as I entered the room, the bell rang. Charlie was on his feet, body gyrating, arms up, fists clenched, first one shoulder, then the next, a swing, then another, feet dancing, and he exclaimed, "Come on, Doc, let's go a few rounds." I couldn't believe it. "Sure Charlie," I said. But then he stopped, and as I approached, he had a strange look in his eye. A deafening silence filled the room and then with lightning speed, he grabbed my tie at the collar and lifted me with one hand onto my tippy-toes.

I seriously feared for my life. I said nothing, I was motionless, then Charlie spoke. "You're no doctor," he said. I was dumbfounded, in milliseconds I recalled my encounter with him just months ago in the reception room; feeble, almost lifeless, the walker, then the cane and now shadowboxing once again. Puzzled I knew I didn't deserve the credit as Dr. Price taught me. But at least I thought I was helping. I was in shock. Then in the next breath, Charlie's words changed my life forever.

"You're no doctor . . . you're a magician!"

Micheil Hanczaryk, D.C.

"I'm curious. Why is this technique called the Holyfield Maneuver?"

CLOSE TO HOME. ©*John McPherson. Reprinted with permission of UNIVERSAL PRESS SYNDICATE. All rights reserved.*

A Mother's Courage

Running through the living room with beads of sweat across his forehead at the age of twelve and enjoying the wonders of summertime, he was stopped by his mother, who had noticed a few red spots on his chest. Upon closer examination she decided it was a simple rash and would remedy this with the ranch-style cure of iodine. Several days had passed before the mother reexamined her son and noticed that the spots, which were in the beginning only about half the size of a dime, had doubled in size and number. The sores were red, itchy and the skin would flake off in dandruff like patches. He told of the strange looks he would get from his classmates at school.

He was taken to a local dermatologist and his mother explained the situation. They were given several salves and told to return in a few weeks. This repeated over several visits and each time the rash seemed to double in the amount of area affected. The itching increased and it was often difficult to relieve. After a few months, it was noted that the boy's skin was actually deeply tanned from the harsh ingredients of the ointments, one of which was cortisone. As he moved about, the skin had a tendency to tear open and bleed due to the dryness.

Not truly happy with the results thus far, it was decided to visit another dermatologist and see if some other substance besides cortisone could be used. The rash, which was identified as Psoriasis, was now covering nearly three quarters of the boy's body. The new doctor did what he could and was very nice, although the rash continued to worsen. After several more weeks went by, there was not an area of the body which was not covered by this insidious rash. He would walk around bent, as if he was a little old man, to keep from tearing his skin.

The young boy was growing weak in health, however, staying strong in spirit. Over the months the young boy spent many moments of prayer looking for some answer to why or what this was about. As the days marched on it was increasingly difficult for him to attend school due to the skin irritation and difficulty moving about. The skin would lose tremendous patches and he would leave a trail of flaked skin wherever he went. The skin, at this point, had lost much of its elasticity and would easily tear rather than stretch. He spent much of his time in a chair sipping water to keep hydrated enough to stay alive.

Until, one day, he began to slip away. His mother, seeing that he was nearly in a coma from dehydration, transported the child to the emergency room at a local hospital. When he was placed on the gurney, the skin where he had been held actually peeled off leaving two bloody handprints on the boy's back from the pressure. The team of doctors began an array of tests on this boy. The doctor who headed up the team even brought in specialists to help sort out the mystery. This fine doctor, who headed up the team, was very experienced and was faced with a most difficult task of telling the mother that although most of the tests were negative, it was not expected that this child live through the night. She stood there for what seemed to be an eternity looking around the room. The room in the hospital, which was to be their last night together, was stark white with chrome trim. The IV in the boy was dripping methodically as the murmur of voices was heard in the background. After much prayer for some kind of answer, some type of help, the two drifted off to sleep.

Fortunately, the doctor's prediction was not true. Early in the morning, well before most were awake—including the sun—the mother decided to take this boy out of the hospital in search of a solution. Much to the discouragement of the hospital staff, she carried her son out and headed down the highway in hopes of some miracle. The car pulled into the parking lot of a chiropractor's office. After hours of waiting, the office finally opened at 9 A.M. She took her son in and the story was explained in great detail. This boy underwent very intensive chiropractic care of about two adjustments a day for over a month. As if by miracle, which can often occur when the life force of the body is restored by removing the interference on it, the boy began to heal. Within six months the boy's skin and health had returned to normal; he was once again able to run, play and enjoy life.

It was quite a miracle at that. How did I come to know this special boy, you may ask? Well, the doctor at the hospital was my father, and I know that he did everything within his power to save his own son. His most difficult moment was to tell my mother that he had no idea how to save their own son. Yes, that boy was me, and had my mother not taken me out of the hospital that night I would not be here today telling this story to my own patients as a doctor of chiropractic.

Bradley Shapero, D.C.

Chiropractic Saved My Legs

A number of years ago a frightened and searching man entered my office. He was hoping that I might be able to help him with his severe diabetic condition. He presented me with bluish-green legs covered with large, deep, circular, unhealing ulcers. His medical doctor had just told him that week that his left leg, and soon his right, needed amputation. He was desperately looking for some form of alternative. He cried, "I don't want to lose my legs. Please help me!" I conducted a history and examination and identified spinal subluxations that I felt were correlating with his condition, as well as patterns of lifestyle that were compromising his health. I felt that I would be able to help him. I realized that he had not ever received conservative chiropractic care before, nor had he previously considered such a natural approach. He had only taken insulin and other medications and lived his life as always.

I correlated my findings and planned for him a series of chiropractic adjustments, a dietary and nutritional supplementation program, an exercise regime, and a plethora of uplifting mental principles and suggestions. I had seen some of my patients respond beautifully before from this approach and felt certain I would help him

I began adjusting his spine three times a week and monitoring his other recommended activities. Although I was confident at first in my adjustment procedures and recommendations, my confidence began to wane as the weeks and months passed by. After six months of care and concentrated attention, I felt that it would be wise for him to consider some other alternative. I was not satisfied with the minimal results we had attained. I sat him down in my office and began to suggest that we seek another approach.

He interrupted me before I could finish, stating, "Dr. Demartini, please tell me you are not dismissing me from care. Please tell me that you will continue to work with me and with my condition. Please continue, for you are helping me."

I explained to him that I was not satisfied with the results; that they had not met my expectations and I felt it was only fair to inform him of my feelings about his condition.

Then, with a very open heart and streaming tears, he stated, "Dr. Demartini, six months ago I was told that I was about to lose my legs and would never walk normally again in my life. But you see, six months later I still have my legs and I can still walk. So please, Dr. Demartini, don't discontinue my adjustments. Don't give up on me. I know you are on track, and it will soon, or someday, heal. Please don't dismiss me. Please, sir."

His certainty was inspiring and moving, to say the least. I felt a renewed sense of hope, so I told him that I would work with him for another six months. But I added that if he showed no more promising signs of improvement, I would again consider referring him out. He agreed.

We worked diligently for the next few months, and gradually, little by little, his ulcers did begin to heal and his discoloration began to clear. At the end of just six more months, his legs returned to normal, his lifestyle had improved, and his outlook on life had become even more inspiring and grateful. He even returned to work. He was deeply thankful for chiropractic, and so was I.

He taught me a great practice lesson involving patience and perseverance. He reminded me, and reconfirmed what I had already believed but needed a reminder of, that *the power that made the body certainly has the power to heal the body.*

From that time on, I realized that I had put too high a level of expectation in too short a time on myself and on my patients' healing potential. So I lengthened my care and set more realistic expectations on my patients and myself. I also learned to be more certain, present, grateful, and loving with my patients. I came to understand how important hope was to people and how chiropractic represented loving hope.

John F. Demartini, D.C.

You Can Tell That?

A colleague was examining a patient using a method of analysis called the Thompson technique. This technique enables the doctor to identify a myriad of things about the body by comparing the changes in the length of each leg as the body is challenged in a number of ways. In fact, it is not uncommon for a patient to be quite surprised at how much insight this technique allows the doctor to gather.

On that day, as he examined the woman's leg lengths, my colleague noticed the distinct odor of gasoline emanating from her shoes.

He commented, "Did you just come from the gas station?"

Immediately, and with a look of complete disbelief, the patient jumped to her feet and remarked, "You can tell THAT from my leg lengths?!"

Ryan R. French, D.C.

"Are you gonna whine, or are you
gonna let me fix your back?!"

CLOSE TO HOME. ©*John McPherson. Reprinted with permission of UNIVERSAL
PRESS SYNDICATE. All rights reserved.*

Living Life to the Fullest

Let us choose to believe something good can happen.

J. Martin Kohe

In 1926, at the age of twelve, I hurt my right lower leg playing soccer. I came from a family of four boys and one girl. My father, Emil Yochum, ran a coal and ice business and was not well off financially, so my parents could not afford to buy me a pair of shin guards. Being a rather agile soccer player and quite speedy when I got the ball, my opponents would kick me in the shins to prevent me from scoring a goal. This happened repeatedly over the course of the summer and I developed an open sore with pain in my shin. I was finally taken to the family doctor where x-rays were taken of my leg and the diagnosis of a pus-producing infection was made.

There were no appropriate drug therapies available during this pre-antibiotic era to arrest this infection, so I was given a series of medications and potions, none of which were of any benefit. The pain was intense and I was not able to bear weight upon the lower extremity and was forced to use crutches. The local general practitioner of medicine came to our home on several occasions, where I was laid upon the kitchen table and the abscess would be lanced. The pus expelled from the lower extremity almost reached the ceiling.

After repeated attempts to curb the infection in this manner failed, the doctor told my parents that the only treatment to prevent the disease from progressing up my leg was amputation below the knee. My parents were horrified at this opinion, as was I. Out of desperation, they took me to John Wedge, a chiropractor in south St. Louis; only one mile from where I was born and grew up. Dr. Wedge examined me and reported that he wasn't at all sure chiropractic could help me, but he certainly wanted to try. An extended series of adjustments, along with nutritional support, hydrotherapy and passive exercise was his treatment recommendation.

I was taken to Dr. Wedge five to six times a week for an entire calendar year. Little by little, and to the amazement of my parents, Dr. Wedge, and myself, the soft tissue of my lower leg gradually showed healing and improvement. Eventually, I was able to walk without pain and gladly threw away the crutches that had crippled my life for close to a year and a half.

My family was overjoyed. The treatment from Dr. Wedge had resulted in increasing my overall host resistance and uplifting my immune system to fight this devastating, life-threatening infection. Dr. Wedge's waiting room was always full, and sitting there five to six days a week for an entire calendar year allowed me to see and talk with many patients seeking relief for all sorts of maladies—back pain, asthma, migraine headaches, menstrual cramps, psoriasis, eczema, sinus problems and untold others. Over the year and a half, I watched with amazement as nearly all of these patients fully recovered to normal health. After my leg was saved, I made a commitment to myself that I wanted to serve mankind in the same way he did. I wanted to be a doctor of chiropractic. After finishing high school, I then attended the Missouri Chiropractic College, graduated, and practiced chiropractic in south St. Louis for forty-five years.

The infection in my leg was arrested and left me with an anatomical short leg of approximately 2 inches, which was diagnosed after appropriate x-rays measured the exact degree of deficiency. This was corrected with both heel and sole lifts on all of my shoes. Unfortunately, my athletic career came to an end. For an outstanding, fast soccer player it was a heartbreaking experience, but I was ever so thankful to Dr. John Wedge, who gave me a new lease on life by saving my leg. His efforts were instrumental in my becoming a committed chiropractor, which, in turn, allowed me to motivate my son to enter the same profession. Had it not been for the tenacity of my father, and if we had followed the opinion of the medical doctor, my leg would have been amputated below the knee. I would have missed the opportunity to live life to its fullest and to be able to serve all my patients through chiropractic care.

Kennth E. Yochum, D.C.,
as told to his son, Terry R. Yochum, D.C., D.A.C.B.R.
and his daughter Kay A. Yochum Morris

I Decided Early On In Life

Each thing is of like form from everlasting and comes round again in its cycle . . .

Marcus Aurelius

I decided early on in life that I wanted to be a chiropractor. I guess I wasn't that typical young boy who dreamed of life as a cowboy or a fireman. Chiropractic had been the primary form of healthcare in my life. My parents first took me to see a chiropractor at the age of six months. Over the years, if I was sick, that is where I would go.

I recall an assignment at the end of fourth grade, the time when you prepared to transition from elementary education to middle school. The teacher had asked us to put together a book which included pictures and memories from the school year. She also asked each of us to try and look to the future and write down what we saw ourselves doing for a living. It was then that I first remember expressing my chiropractic desire. I remember the confused looks and questions that came from many of my classmates. "What's a chiropractor?'" "What do they do?" I was astounded that most kids had no idea what a chiropractor was. My early experiences lead me to think everyone went to a chiropractor.

In the summer of 1984, I fulfilled my dream of becoming a doctor of chiropractic. After the graduation ceremony, my family, and my then fiancés family, went out to dinner to celebrate. We had reservations at a small midwestern restaurant that I had never been to, nor seen before. Seated next to us was a table of four people; an older couple accompanied by a younger couple. I recall the restaurant being so cramped that it seemed these people were a part of our party. After having eaten, I began to open a few gifts that I had been given. One particular gift was a wooden statue of a doctor holding up an x-ray with one hand while holding a model of a spine with the other. It was upon seeing this statue that the elderly lady sitting at the table next to us inquired as to what we were celebrating. I told her that I had just graduated from Chiropractic College. She smiled, offered her congratulations and proceeded to inform us that her husband, the man sitting to my left, was also a chiropractor. At that moment my mother spoke with a look of wonder on her face. "Dr. Solomon?" she asked. "Why, yes, I am," the gray haired man replied equally puzzled.

My mother looked at me and went on to explain that Dr. Solomon was that first chiropractor that had adjusted me when I was a baby. Here I was, on my graduation day, sitting shoulder to shoulder with my first chiropractic experience. To make matters even stranger, Dr. Solomon had retired and moved to Florida. He was back only for the weekend to celebrate a family birthday.

Was it just a coincidence? Graduation day, the same restaurant, and one table away? Or was it a sign of destiny, the passing of the proverbial chiropractic torch from one generation to the next. (Actually, Dr. Solomon did pass me the dinner rolls but the torch metaphor sounds better.)

I'm still not sure why, as a little kid, I chose chiropractic as my profession and life's work; I think it may have chosen me.

Kevin W. Paustian D.C.

More Chicken Soup?

Many of the stories you have read in this book were submitted by readers like you who had read earlier *Chicken Soup for the Soul* books. We publish at least five or six *Chicken Soup for the Soul* books every year. We invite you to contribute a story to one of these future volumes.

Stories may be up to 1,200 words and must uplift or inspire. You may submit an original piece, something you have read or your favorite quotation on your refrigerator door.

To obtain a copy of our submission guidelines and a listing of upcoming *Chicken Soup for the Soul* books, please write, fax or check our Web site.

Please send your submissions to:

www.chickensoup.com
Chicken Soup for the Soul
P.O. Box 30880, Santa Barbara, CA 93130
fax: 805-563-2945

To submit a chiropractic story or to order additional copies of this book please visit us at *www.chickensoup. parkerseminars.com*

Just send a copy of your stories and other pieces to the above address.

We will be sure that both you and the author are credited for your submission.

For information about speaking engagements, other books, audiotapes, workshops and training programs, please see the following pages.

Who Is Jack Canfield?

Jack Canfield is one of America's leading experts in the development of human potential and personal effectiveness. He is both a dynamic, entertaining speaker and a highly sought-after trainer. Jack has a wonderful ability to inform and inspire audiences toward increased levels of self-esteem and peak performance.

He is the author and narrator of several bestselling audio- and videocassette programs, including *Self-Esteem and Peak Performance, How to Build Maximum Confidence, Self-Esteem in the Classroom* and *Chicken Soup for the Soul—Live*. He is regularly seen on television shows such as *Good Morning America, 20/20* and *NBC Nightly News*. Jack has co-authored numerous books, including the *Chicken Soup for the Soul* series, *Dare to Win, The Aladdin Factor, 100 Ways to Build Self-Concept in the Classroom, Heart at Work* and *The Power of Focus*.

Jack is a regularly featured speaker for professional associations, school districts, government agencies, churches, hospitals, sales organizations and corporations. His clients have included the American Dental Association, the American Management Association, AT&T, Campbell's Soup, Clairol, Domino's Pizza, GE, ITT, Hartford Insurance, Johnson & Johnson, the Million Dollar Roundtable, NCR, New England Telephone, Re/Max, Scott Paper, TRW and Virgin Records.

Jack conducts an annual eight-day Training of Trainers program in the areas of self-esteem and peak performance. It attracts educators, counselors, parenting trainers, corporate trainers, professional speakers, ministers and others interested in developing their speaking and seminar-leading skills.

For further information about Jack's books, tapes and training programs, or to schedule him for a presentation, please contact:

Self-Esteem Seminars
P.O. Box 30880
Santa Barbara, CA 93130
phone: 805-563-2935 • fax: 805-563-2945
Web site: *www.chickensoup.com*

Who Is Mark Victor Hansen?

Mark Victor Hansen is a professional speaker who in the last twenty years has made over 4,000 presentations to more than 2 million people in thirty-two countries. His presentations cover sales excellence and strategies; personal empowerment and development; and how to triple your income and double your time off.

Mark has spent a lifetime dedicated to his mission of making a profound and positive difference in people's lives. Throughout his career, he has inspired hundreds of thousands of people to create a more powerful and purposeful future for themselves while stimulating the sale of billions of dollars worth of goods and services.

Mark is a prolific writer and has authored *Future Diary*, *How to Achieve Total Prosperity* and *The Miracle of Tithing*. He is coauthor of the *Chicken Soup for the Soul* series, *Dare to Win* and *The Aladdin Factor* (all with Jack Canfield), and *The Master Motivator* (with Joe Batten).

Mark has also produced a complete library of personal-empowerment audio- and videocassette programs that have enabled his listeners to recognize and use their innate abilities in their business and personal lives. His message has made him a popular television and radio personality, with appearances on ABC, NBC, CBS, HBO, PBS and CNN. He has also appeared on the cover of numerous magazines, including *Success*, *Entrepreneur* and *Changes*.

Mark is a big man with a heart and spirit to match—an inspiration to all who seek to better themselves.

For further information about Mark, write:

MVH & Associates
P.O. Box 7665
Newport Beach, CA 92658
phone: 714-759-9304 or 800-433-2314
fax: 714-722-6912
Web site: *www.chickensoup.com*

Who Is Dr. Fabrizio Mancini?

Dr. Fabrizio Mancini is a family man, an internationally acclaimed professional speaker, educator, president of one of the leading Chiropractic Schools in the world, healer, philanthropist and volunteer in many local and national groups.

He came to the United States in 1978 from Colombia, South America. His dream was to become a Doctor so he may help in the suffering of others. His journey began in Dallas as he studied Pre-Medicine at the prestigious University of Dallas where he was preparing to be a neurosurgeon. He later discovered the Chiropractic profession and enrolled as a student in 1987, as he recognized the potential in preventing disease and educating your patients in a wellness lifestyle for optimum performance. He began the Mancini Chiropractic Center in 1993 in Dallas, Texas and has been serving thousands of patients until this day.

Today, Dr. Mancini spends most of his time leading the Parker College of Chiropractic in historic accomplishments in education and professional and personal seminars. He also travels the world inspiring thousands of people each year with his message of success, service, health and wellness. But when asked, he would say his favorite time is being with his beautiful wife, Alicia, and his two sons, Gianni and Luciano.

Dr. Mancini has received many recognitions such as Heroes for Humanity Award, Vision Award, High-Spirited Citizen Award, Rising Star Award, Crystal Apple Educators Award, Extra-Ordinary Speaker Award, Award of Honor, Who's Who to name a few. He has been the guest of many radio and television programs. He also has given testimony to the White House Commission for Complimentary and Alternative Medicine. He has author many articles in various journals and has been featured in newsapers and magazines nationwide.

For further information on Dr. Mancini or to inquire about a speaking engagement, please contact:

PCC/Dr. Mancini
2500 Walnut Hill Lane
Dallas, Texas 75229
phone: 214-902-3470
fax: 214-352-6603
e-mail: *president@parkercc.edu*
Web sites: *www.parkercc.edu* and *www.parkerseminars.com*

Contributors

Several of the stories in this book were taken from previously published sources, such as books, magazines and newspapers. These sources are acknowledged in the permissions section. If you would like to contact any of the contributors for information about their writing, or would like to invite them to speak in your community, look for their contact information included in their biography.

Dr. John Adams is the author of *The Power*, a medical thriller about a chiropractor who exposes a corrupt pharmaceutical company. The Power is available through Amazon.com or *www.john-adams.net*. Also watch for *Burning Faith*, the saga of a Southern California midwife under attack from the medical birthing establishment.

Stuart "Terry" Bartow is happily married to Sandy, and is father to Tim 15, (subject of *A Father's Story*), Elliot 16, Katie 12 and Samantha 10. Mr. Bartow also has two stepsons, Bryon and Bill and four grandchildren. He is Headmaster of St. Paul's Episcopal Day School in Kansas City, Missouri. Contact: *terry@speds.org*.

Dr. Randy Baze graduated with honors from Sherman College of Straight Chiropractic in 1983. His office is located in Renton, Washington where he runs a high volume people practice. In addition, he cares for a steady stream of animals on a donation basis, sending all proceeds to his alma mater.

Richard Betts received his Bachelor of Arts from Viterbo University and completes his chiropractic degree from Life University in 2004. He writes, directs and produces inspirational children's plays and musicals. Along with working on chiropractic books for children he enjoys traveling, rollerblading and communicating the importance of chiropractic. Please email him at: *dr_betts@hotmail.com*

Steven Blevins graduated from Palmer College with a Doctorate in Chiropractic in 1988. He is in private practice in Illinois. Steven enjoys giving back to his community by his involvement in the Jaycees and to the nation while serving as a member of the U.S. Army Reserve since 1980.

Catherine Boykin is a stay-home mom of two beautiful daughters, Kellie Anne and Kaitlyn. Prior to that she enjoyed a 10-year career in systems technology. She now devotes all of her time to her family, riding horses, volunteering at school or church, and dabbling in freelance writing. She also manages her husband's chiropractic office. She has the best of both worlds—working from home and being with her children. For this, she thanks the Lord.

Jeffrey D. Conner, D.C., is a 1995 Parker graduate. His belief in the natural capability of the body to heal itself motivated him to get involved with a company that specializes in individual customized vitamins. He is a testimony to the effectiveness of this product. Please reach him at (602) 993-0131 or email *azchoicechiro@mindspring.com*.

Randall Cooper is married to Rebecca and they have a daughter, Emily. They all love the outdoors and hope to experience more of the rocky mountains of Canada very soon. Please reach Randal at: *rrecooper@hotmail.com*.

Dr. Frank A. Corbo is the co-founder and senior editor of *Chiropractic Wellness and Fitness Magazine*. He received his Bachelor of Arts from Lafayette College in 1985 and his Doctorate in Chiropractic, with honors, from Los Angeles College of Chiropractic in 1995. He is happily married to his wonderful wife Wynnie, and has three beautiful daughters, Mikayla, Victoria and Nicole. He can be reached at *DrCorbo@aol.com*.

Peter Cranton, D.C., Life University, 1998. Dr. Cranton holds an undergraduate degree from Rollins College, FL and a master's degree in Architecture from Auburn University. Besides cartooning and painting, Peter enjoys writing and performing inspirational children's music. He owns and operates Peachtree Battle Chiropractic in Atlanta, GA. Email him at: *prcranton@aol.com*.

Dr. Jeff Danielson received his B.A. from UCLA and D.C. from CCCLA. He lives in Prior Lake, MN. He directs a high volume chiropractic clinic in Burnsville, MN and recently started a company called Big Fish Promotions which offers many success products for all businesses. Email him at *spinemanj@earthlink.net*.

Dr. John F. Demartini is a chiropractor that has spoken, taught, consulted or counseled on 6 continents, in 32 countries to over 410 million people. He has written over 100 books, including the best selling book entitled *Count Your Blessings—The Healing Power of Gratitude and Love* and his newest arrival *The Breakthrough Experience, A Revolutionary New Approach to Personal Transformation*. *www.drdemartini.com*.

Sarah Dixon-Emerick is a Pennsylvania native, where she worked as an office manager for a chiropractor for nearly three years. She has recently married and now resides in Virginia with her husband, Jonathan. Sarah currently works as a chiropractic assistant for a chiropractor in Richmond. If you wish to contact Sarah, please do so via e-mail at: *sjdixonom@yahoo.com*

Sara Downey is a 1994 graduate of Parker Chiropractic College, and is practicing in Grand Prairie, Texas. Her deep interest in wellness and nutrition is a focus of her community involvement. She enjoys reading, writing, participation in the fine arts, and traveling with her husband, Patrick, to explore museums and galleries. Her plans for future travel will focus on Colorado, to enjoy her first grandchild, Morgan Joy! She can be reached at *downy605@aol.com*.

Dr. Ryan French received his Doctor of Chiropractic degree from the Canadian

Memorial Chiropractic College in 2000. He currently runs a family-based practice in Bolton, Ontario. Please reach him at Inside Out Family Chiropractic: 905-951 9911.

Amanda K. Gagnon is a theatre major at Christopher Newport University. She has been inspired throughout her life by her father William K. Renas and his alternative healthcare practice. She knows that through chiropractic a higher level of physical and mental well-being can be achieved.

Dr. Barry Gardner is a 1993 Parker College graduate. Dr. Gardner lectures on varied health topics. He and his wife Cyndie treat patients at their Tulsa, OK clinic. They enjoy traveling, camping and spending time with the Lord. Contact him at (918) 663-6045. Email *docbwginok@cs.com*.

Mary Beth Garrison is a Communications graduate, and has spent 25 years writing for television, radio and print mediums throughout the United States. She lives in the Tehachapi Mountains with husband Tim, daughter Becca, and their dachshund Shatzie. A chiropractic convert, she gets adjusted to battle her sometimes out-of-control schedule.

Gene Giggleman received his Doctor of Veterinary Medicine degree from Texas A&M University in 1981. He has been in private practice and has taught at Parker College of Chiropractic for the past 20 years. He began adjusting his animal patients over 13 years ago.

Morris Goodman, "The Miracle Man", grew up and was educated in the Virginia Beach, Virginia area where he currently resides with his wife Cathy. He travels the world speaking to audiences of all types and may be reached at Miracle Man Productions, 4176 Cheswick Lane, Virginia Beach, VA 23455. (757) 473-8175.

Micheil Hanczaryk, B.A., D.C. is the director of the Bristol Chiropractic Centre, P.C. specializing in neuromusculoskeletal health conditions. He is also the founder of Strategic Operating Systems (S.O.S.), a consulting firm dedicated to providing high-quality professional development for doctors and their staff. He is one of the most sought-after speakers in the chiropractic profession, a co-author of *The Seven Steps to Success, Volume I and II* and voted chiropractor of the year. For more information call S.O.S. at (810) 733-1261, write the company at 5098 W. Bristol Road, Flint, MI 48507 or email to *nuspine@aol.com*.

Dr. Richard L. Hartman received his Doctorate, with honors, from the prestigious Palmer College of Chiropractic in 1959. He remains active in practice and many continuing education programs. He has published *The Vertebral Subluxation Complex*, a report of findings charts used in thousands of chiropractic offices worldwide. His contact information is: 1201 Harrison Street Philadelphia, PA 19124. Phone: 215-744-4430 Fax: 215-744-9606. Email: *drrlhartman@aol.com*

John Holland received his doctor of Chiropractic degree from Los Angeles College of Chiropractic in 1989. He has a family chiropractic office in La Habra, California. John has written a number of children stories to teach, inspire and encourage his own five children. He considers his greatest decision in life to be the beautiful wife he chose over twenty years ago. He loves any family time, golfing, writing and helping people feel better. Please email him at: *johnhholland@earthlink.net*.

Ginger Hotard Humphries graduated as a Medical Secretary from City College in 1994. Ginger's experience includes Outreach Counselor to Native Americans, Chiropractic Assistant, PR, Development and Office Management. Ginger enjoys working with children and adults, socializing with family and friends, reading, traveling, bicycling, gardening, yoga and swimming.

Donald K. Kase is the co-founder and Editor-in-Chief of *Chiropractic Wellness and Fitness Magazine*. For over twenty years he has designed and created over 100 magazine titles including *AVID Golfer Magazine*. He resides in sunny Southern California with his beautiful wife, Kristina and their daughter Melissa. He can be reached at *Dkase@sbcglobal.net*.

Dr. Kyle Kelbert attended the University of Manitoba before earning a Bachelor of Science and Doctor of Chiropractic degrees in Minneapolis. He returned to his hometown, Flin Flon, Manitoba, to establish his chiropractic clinic and continues to pursue writing while in private practice. Contact: 416 Parkway Blvd., Flin Flon, MB, Canada R8A OK6 or *kkelbert@hotmail.com*.

Annette Klosler currently resides in Southwest Ontario, Canada with her husband and Lauren who is now four years old. In 2001 they were all blessed with a second little miracle and a sister for Lauren. Annette is a Bank Manager for a leading financial institution and in her spare time enjoys spending time with her family, running and scrap booking.

Michael Kohler graduated magna cum laude from Southern California College of Chiropractic in 1989, and was class valedictorian. He has been in private practice in Northern San Diego County since 1990. Dr. Kohler lives in Carlsbad where he enjoys spending time with his wife and exercising outdoors.

Dr. Tedd Koren speaks and writes on chiropractic, health philosophy, the childhood immunization controversy, natural healing and related topics. He is well known for his chiropractic patient education materials at Koren Publications (*www.korenpublications.com*). He recently founded the Foundation For Health Choice (*www.foundationforhealthchoice.com*) that is fighting for health care freedom. Write to Dr. Koren at *tkoren1@aol.com*.

Jeannine Marie L'Heureux received her M.A. from the University of New Hampshire in 1987. She is currently the Office Manager at Windman Chiropractic and is enrolled in The On-Line Bible College. Jeannine has written several devotionals and plans to write her autobiography. Please e-mail her at *janelle1@bellatlantic.net*.

Dr. Mark David Lagerkvist is a noted chiropractor, consultant, lecturer and seminar leader committed to helping people transform their minds, bodies and souls through Life Works Ltd. A corporation consisting of Life Works

Consultanting, Life Line Chiropractic, Life Path Retreats and Seminars, Life Essentials Luxury Supplements and Life Works Financial. All of which support human beings in discovering and fulfilling mission. Dr. Mark can be reached at *www.askdoctormark.com* or 708-205-8872.

Susie Latham is the mother of three children, two now in college. She owns her own business, a Nail and Tanning Salon in the small town where they live. She and her husband have been married for 23 years now and look forward to many more years ahead and hopefully without too much pain as they stay well adjusted.

Buddy Levy, M.A., B.A., Creative Writing and Literature, University of Idaho is a book author and freelance writer who covers adventure, nature, and outdoor subjects extensively. He is Senior Instructor of English at Washington State University, where he teaches writing. Please reach him at *writer@buddylevy.com*, or visit his website *www.buddylevy.com*.

Dr. Jane Lock is located outside of Philadelphia, Pennsylvania. She uses NET's emotional corrections as part of a comprehensive approach in treating her patients, along with low-force adjusting, nutrition, homeopathy and herbs. She can be reached at (610) 948-0323 and recommends NET's website: *www.netmindbody.com*.

Christine Maguire received her Bachelor of Arts in Psychology from Providence College in Rhode Island in 1991. She received her Doctor of Chiropractic Degree from Logan College in St. Louis, Missouri in 1994. She is currently practicing chiropractic in Maine.

Dr. Larry Markson did indeed run a very successful Chiropractic practice for 20 years and then went on to become Chairman & CEO of The Masters Circle, a Chiropractic Leadership Coaching and Practice Building organization that has served more than 9,000 over the past 22 years. (*www.themasterscircle.com*)

Dr. Joel Miller is a 1983 cum laude graduate from Life University. He has been in private practice for the past 19 years. He is the former lead professor in Pediatric Adjusting and the associate professor in Pediatric Clinical Assessment at Life University. He was the recipient of the Outstanding Chiropractic Leadership Award in 2002. Dr. Miller speaks regularly throughout North America and may be contacted at *DrJKidsDC@hotmail.com*.

Dr. April Nelson is a 1998 graduate of Texas Chiropractic College. She is in private practice in Clear Lake, Texas where her passion for caring for children and pregnant women is evident. She is currently being certified as a pediatric chiropractor and has a goal of becoming a leading pediatric chiropractic expert.

Dr. Kevin Paustian received his Doctor of Chiropractic degree, with honors, from Palmer College of Chiropractic in 1984. He maintains a private practice in Durant, Iowa as well as being a member of the Palmer College faculty. Dr. Paustian and his wife Brenda have three children. In his free time he enjoys traveling, golfing, music and art.

Dr. Laura Peterson of Family Health Chiropractic resides and practices in Folsom, California. She strives to bring health to children and adults of her community through the natural approach of Chiropractic, creating better-health for a better life. She can be reached at 24988 Blue Ravine Road, Suite 106, Folsom, CA 95630 or (916) 355-0440.

Dr. Brenda Pfeiffer is a 1994 graduate of Northwestern Health Sciences University in Bloomington, MN. She runs a family chiropractic clinic in Wyoming, MN. Outside the office, she enjoys running, riding motorcycles, good conversation and spending time with her two dogs and cat.

Dr. Carol Phillips is an internationally renowned lecturer in the field of chiropractic and craniosacral therapy, author of *Hands of Love: Seven Steps to the Miracle of Birth* and executive producer of *Hands of Love: Witnessing the Miracle of Birth.* Contact information can be found on her website at *www.newdawnpublish.com.*

Dawn Planty is a chiropractic assistant/office manager for Dr. Jeffrey D. Conner. She is active with C.A.N., a chiropractic assistant networking group in Phoenix, AZ. Together with Dr. Conner she promotes individual customized vitamins and supplements. Please reach her at (602) 993-0131 or email *azchoicechiro@mindspring.com* for more information.

Dr. Eric Plasker is founder and CEO of The Family Practice, Inc., which provides premiere coaching and training for chiropractors worldwide. Internationally recognized as a speaker and educator, he is best known for rallying chiropractors and the public around the Lifetime Care for Everyone (LCfE) and Family Wellness visions. Visit *www.thefamilypractice.net* or e-mail: *drplasker@thefamilypractice.net.*

Dr. Pawel Pyrda is a graduate of NYCC. He is bilingual and enjoys working on families. Dr. Pyrda had post-graduate work in applied Kinesiology, BioSET, Allergy Elimination Technique and Reiki. Pawel has participated in numerous fireworks, drumming circles and sweat lodges. Email him at *Pawel@Annes WellnessCenter.com.*

Gil Ramirez graduated from Cleveland C.C.L.A in 1955 and opened his practice in Orange County. He moved to Oakhurst, CA near Yosemite Park in 1978 and is still practicing Chiropractic there. Gil is married to Annette and they have 4 grown children.

Dr. William Remling received his chiropractic degree in 1963 from the Chiropractic Institute of NY. He was in private practice for over 35 years. A lecturer, author, and chiropractic consultant, he lives in Louisville, KY with his wife, Kathy. He can be reached at: *GetMeHealthy@aol.com.*

Caroline Reno received her Bachelor of Science in Physiology at UC Davis, California in 1996. She received her Doctor of Chiropractic degree, with Magna Cum Laude honors, at Cleveland Chiropractic College of Los Angeles in 2001. She enjoys skiing, traveling and art museums. Please reach her at *DrCReno@aol.com.*

Christine Rockel recently received her Doctorate from Parker College of Chiropractic. She will be practicing in Missouri following National Board exams. She enjoys spending time with her two beautiful daughters Brittney (14) and Blakely (10).

Terry A. Rondberg, D.C., is president of the World Chiropractic Alliance, publisher of *The Chiropractic Journal* and author of the popular book *Chiropractic First*. After graduating from Logan Chiropractic College, he opened a private practice in St. Louis, where he dedicated himself to his life-long ambition of creating a subluxation-free world. Dr. Rondberg can be reached at *tarondberg@worldchiropracticalliance.org.*

Cindy Sapp was born and raised in the Detroit area and attended Grand Valley University near Grand Rapids. Married to Danny, she is the mother of 4 children, Christopher, Christina, Marcus and Mariah. Cindy is a Deputy Sheriff who enjoys spending time with her family and their dog Shadow.

Kurt R. Schaarschmidt, D.C. received his Doctor of Chiropractic degree from Palmer College of Chiropractic. He has been practicing in West Bend, Wisconsin since 1976 and has a multiple doctor clinic. Kurt enjoys reading, boating, traveling, and sharing his inspirational and natural health care knowledge with others. Please e-mail him at *castlecare@schaarschmidt.com.*

Dr. Bradley Shapero, doctor of chiropractic, has a highly successful practice fulfilling his purpose to help as many people as possible to obtain and maintain optimum health and well being, naturally, with chiropractic care and lifestyle education. Contact him at *DrShapero@PremierHealthCareSC.com* or visit his website at *www.PremierHealthCareSC.com.*

Dr. David Singer received his undergraduate degree from Rutger's University, his M.S. degree in nutrition from the University of Bridgeport, and his doctorate from the New York College of Chiropractic. Dr. Singer founded his own consulting company, which has twice won the prestigious INC. Magazine's Top 100 Fastest Growing Companies award. He is currently on the advisory board for both In Practice magazine and The American Chiropractor. In 1999, he received the "Person of the Year Award" for having the most economically influential impact on the Chiropractic profession. One of Dr. Singer's major goals is to see that Chiropractic can become "The number one health care choice in the world."

Dr. Pamela Stone is in private practice in Kennesaw, GA. The focus of her practice is promoting health and wellness among children and adults, allowing them to experience optimal health. She has completed five marathons and more than 40 triathlons, and credits regular chiropractic care for allowing her to be healthy and injury-free. She can be reached at (770) 517-4769 or at *DrPStone@mindspring.com.*

Sheryl Tollenaar received her Doctor of Chiropractic degree, as well as a Bachelors of Science, with a major in Anatomy, from Parker College of

Chiropractic. Sheryl enjoys traveling, especially to foreign countries, as well as learning foreign languages. She plans to publish a party planning book in the future, including recipes. Please email her at *sltchiro@hotmail.com*.

Gloria Updyke is working toward her doctorate of Education at University of Sarasota. She and her husband, Warne Nelson, are committed pet lovers and backcountry travelers. She has climbed over 60 of the highest peaks in the east, is a competitive powerlifter, and loves watching sunsets from their porch swing.

Dr. Jens Valle graduated from Life Chiropractic College (now Life University) in March of 1988. His practice, Action Chiropractic Center, is located in Acworth, Georgia. Dr. Valle enjoys the rewards he receives by adjusting families and helping them express their God given potential. Please reach him at: *JValle4@bellsouth.net*

Dr. Richard Walford is a family chiropractor that loves sports. His dream has come true through helping the Olympic hopefuls at the local Olympic Training Center with chiropractic. Dr. Walford is also a sports dad to his volleyball-playing daughters.

Eva Wallert was a Radiology Supervisor for a metropolitan hospital when she met her husband, Wayne Wallert, D.C., 23 years ago. Assimilating from a medical background to natural, safe Chiropractic came easily. Eva graduated from Parker Chiropractic College's Chiropractic Assistant program and has been the office manager/C.A. at the Ellsworth Chiropractic Clinic since 1983. The Wallert's have 5 children and 5 grandchildren. Their youngest son, Joe earns his D.C. in April 2003.

John G. Watson graduated from Palmer College. At that time he and his wife had 10 children. He now has 13 children and 26 grandchildren—and counting. He is practicing in Hendersonville, NC, and utilizes Activator, BEST, Flexion Disctration and PST. Reach him at: (828) 693-3310 or *chirowatson@juno.com*.

Dr. Leslie Windman is a Board Certified Atlas Orthogonist. She received her doctorate degree in Chiropractic with honors from Palmer University. She is in private practice in Maryland. She has published numerous articles and has appeared on television and radio regarding her work. Her email is *drlwind man@hotmail.com*

Dr. Terry R. Yochum, a second generation Chiropractor and a cum laude graduate of the National College of Chiropractic, is currently the director of the Rocky Mountain Chiropractic Radiological Center in Denver, CO. He has presented over 1000 lectures worldwide and is the author of *Essentials of Skeletal Radiology* with the third edition soon to be ready for publication.

Permissions *(continued from page iv)*

Chiropractic Got Me to the Boston Marathon. Reprinted by permission of Pamela Stone. ©2001 Pamela Stone.

A Daring Adventure. Reprinted by permission of Gloria Updyke. ©2001 Gloria Updyke.

Vertigo, Apnea and *Adding Life to Life.* Reprinted by permission of John Holland. ©2003 John Holland.

The One Who Walked Away! The Miracle Man. Reprinted by permission of Donald K. Kase. ©2003 Donald K. Kase.

The Miracle. Reprinted by permission of Richard L. Hartman, D.C. ©1986 Richard L. Hartman, D.C.

The Battle Within a Man. Reprinted by permission of Sarah Dixon-Emerick. ©2001 Sarah Dixon-Emerick.

Do You Believe in Miracles? Reprinted by permission of Annette Klosler. ©1999 Annette Klosler.

Return to Sanity and *Hospital Rounds.* Reprinted by permission of Tedd Koren, D.C. ©2000, 2002 Tedd Koren, D.C.

In-Flight Adjustment. Reprinted by permission of Dr. David Singer. ©2002 Dr. David Singer.

The Power That Made the Body Heals the Body. Reprinted by permission of Mark Lagerkvist. ©2002 Mark Lagerkvist.

Faith in Chiropractic. Reprinted by permission of Gilbert Ramirez. ©2002 Gilbert Ramirez.

Restored Faith and *Let's Give It a Shot.* Reprinted by permission of Jeffrey Danielson. ©2002 Jeffrey Danielson.

Can You Turn It Back Off? Reprinted by permission of John Watson, D.C. ©2001 John Watson, D.C.

Turning Nightmares into Dreams. Reprinted by permission of Dr. Kyle Kelbert. ©2001 Dr. Kyle Kelbert.

Journey to Freedom From Pain and *A Family Affair.* Reprinted by permission of Frank Corbo. ©2002 Frank Corbo.

Life Is Great. Reprinted by permission of Michael Kohler. ©2002 Michael Kohler.

A Life Changed Once—and Again. Reprinted by permission of Mary Beth Garrison and Susie Latham. ©2001 Mary Beth Garrison.

The Unborn Child. Reprinted by permission of Catherine Boykin. ©2001 Catherine Boykin.

Healing Hands and *Dalton's Smile.* Reprinted by permission of Sara Aurora Downey. ©2001 Sara Aurora Downey.

Please Help My Baby. Reprinted by permission of Richard Betts. ©2001 Richard Betts.

Awakened. Reprinted by permission of Christine Rockel. ©1993 Christine Rockel.

Nobody Likes A Colicky Baby. Reprinted by permission of Kurt Schaarschmidt, D.C. ©2003 Kurt Schaarschmidt, D.C.

Jacob's Story. Reprinted by permission of Eric Plasker, D.C. ©2003 Eric Plasker, D.C.

Can I Have a Cookie? Reprinted by permission of Jens Valle D.C. ©2003 Jens Valle D.C.

A Changed Demeanor. Reprinted by permission of Barry Gardner, D.C. ©2002 Barry Gardner, D.C.

Angel. Reprinted by permission of Carol Phillips. ©2002 Carol Phillips.

Turning On the Power. Reprinted by permission of John Adams, D.C. ©2002 John Adams, D.C.

Healing a Dampened Heart. Reprinted by permission of Amanda K. Gagnon. ©2000 Amanda K. Gagnon.

Now I Know That Grandma Loves Me . . . . Reprinted by permission of Pawel Pyrda, D.C. ©2002 Pawel Pyrda, D.C.

The Big Picture. Reprinted by permission of Richard Walford. ©2000 Richard Walford.

Confidence to Conquer the World. Reprinted by permission of Jeannine Marie L'Heureux and Leslie Windman, D.C. ©2002 Jeannine Marie L'Heureux and Leslie Windman, D.C.

Chicken Soup Is Great . . . But Chiropractic Is Better. Reprinted by permission of Dr. Larry Markson. ©2002 Dr. Larry Markson.

The Things We Don't Do. Reprinted by permission of Steven Blevins. ©2001 Steven Blevins.

I Love Being a Chiropractor. Reprinted by permission of Christine Maguire. ©2002 Christine Maguire.

A Neighbor's Encounter. Reprinted by permission of April Nelson, D.C. ©2001 April Nelson, D.C.

A Father's Story. Reprinted by permission of Terry Bartow. ©2003 Terry Bartow.

Asthma. Reprinted by permission of Cynthia Sapp. ©1996 Cynthia Sapp.

Safe—Inside and Out. Reprinted by permission of Jane M. Lock, D.C. ©2002 Jane M. Lock, D.C.

A Mother's First Kiss. Reprinted by permission of William Remling, D.C. ©2002 William Remling, D.C.

A Lesson in Dignity. Reprinted by permission of Randy Baze. ©1998 Randy Baze.

"Face" Restored. Reprinted by permission of Eva Wallert. ©2000 Eva Wallert.

Nana and Gump. Reprinted by permission of Randal Cooper. ©2001 Randal Cooper.

Casey's First Adjustment. Reprinted by permission of Brenda Pfeiffer. ©2001 Brenda Pfeiffer.

Adjusting to a Better Life. Reprinted by permission of Terry Rondberg, D.C. ©1998 Terry Rondberg, D.C.

A Dog Named Sparky. Reprinted by permission of Gene Giggleman, D.V.M. ©2002 Gene Giggleman, D.V.M.

The Calling. Reprinted by permission of Ginger Hotard Humphries. ©2002 Ginger Hotard Humphries.

A Hidden Miracle. Reprinted by permission of Laura Peterson, D.C. ©2003 Laura Peterson, D.C.

Gangster To Graduate. Reprinted by permission of Sheryl Tollenaar. ©2001 Sheryl Tollenaar.

You're No Doctor. Reprinted by permission of Micheil Hanczaryk, D.C. ©2003 Micheil Hanczaryk, D.C.

A Mother's Courage. Reprinted by permission of Bradley Shapero. ©2001 Bradley Shapero.

Chiropractic Saved My Legs. Reprinted by permission of Dr. John F. Demartini. ©1999 Dr. John F. Demartini.

You Can Tell That? Reprinted by permission of Dr. Ryan R. French. ©2002 Dr. Ryan R. French.

Living Life to the Fullest. Reprinted by permission of Dr. Terry Yochum. ©2003 Dr. Terry Yochum.

I Decided Early On In Life. Reprinted by permission of Kevin Paustian. ©2002 Kevin Paustian.